THE ELECTROSTATICS
OF
BIOLOGICAL CELL MEMBRANES

FRONTIERS OF BIOLOGY

VOLUME 8

Under the General Editorship of

A. NEUBERGER

London

and

E. L. TATUM

New York

NORTH-HOLLAND PUBLISHING COMPANY

AMSTERDAM

THE ELECTROSTATICS
OF
BIOLOGICAL CELL MEMBRANES

ROBERT M. FRIEDENBERG

Associate Professor
The Psychiatric Institute
The University of Maryland
School of Medicine
Baltimore, Maryland

Formerly, Assistant Professor
Center for Theoretical Biology
State University of New York at Buffalo, New York

1967

NORTH-HOLLAND PUBLISHING COMPANY – AMSTERDAM
JOHN WILEY & SONS, INC. – NEW YORK
(Interscience Publishers Division)

PUBLISHERS:

NORTH-HOLLAND PUBLISHING COMPANY – AMSTERDAM

SOLE DISTRIBUTORS FOR U.S.A. AND CANADA:

INTERSCIENCE PUBLISHERS, a division of

JOHN WILEY & SONS, INC. – NEW YORK

PRINTED IN THE NETHERLANDS

Editors' preface

The aim of the publication of this series of monographs, known under the collective title of '*Frontiers of Biology*', is to present coherent and up-to-date views of the fundamental concepts which dominate modern biology.

Biology in its widest sense has made very great advances during the past decade, and the rate of progress has been steadily accelerating. Undoubtedly important factors in this acceleration have been the effective use by biologists of new techniques, including electron microscopy, isotopic labels, and a great variety of physical and chemical techniques, especially those with varying degrees of automation. In addition, scientists with partly physical or chemical backgrounds have become interested in the great variety of problems presented by living organisms. Most significant, however, increasing interest in and understanding of the biology of the cell, especially in regard to the molecular events involved in genetic phenomena and in metabolism and its control, have led to the recognition of patterns common to all forms of life from bacteria to Man. These factors and unifying concepts have led to a situation in which the sharp boundaries between the various classical biological disciplines are rapidly disappearing.

Thus, while scientists are becoming increasingly specialized in their techniques, to an increasing extent they need an intellectual and conceptual approach on a wide and non-specialized basis. It is with these considerations and needs in mind that this series of monographs, '*Frontiers of Biology*' has been conceived.

The advances in various areas of biology, including microbiology, biochemistry, genetics, cytology, and cell structure and function in general will be presented by authors who have themselves contributed significantly to these developments. They will have, in this series, the

5

opportunity of bringing together, from diverse sources, theories and experimental data, and of integrating these into a more general conceptual framework. It is unavoidable, and probably even desirable, that the special bias of the individual authors will become evident in their contributions. Scope will also be given for presentation of new and challenging ideas and hypotheses for which complete evidence is at present lacking. However, the main emphasis will be on fairly complete and objective presentation of the more important and more rapidly advancing aspects of biology. The level will be advanced, directed primarily to the needs of the graduate student and research worker.

Most monographs in this series will be in the range of 200-300 pages, but on occasion a collective work of major importance may be included somewhat exceeding this figure. The intent of the publishers is to bring out these books promptly and in fairly quick succession.

It is on the basis of all these various considerations that we welcome the opportunity of supporting the publication of the series '*Frontiers of Biology*' by North-Holland Publishing Company.

A. NEUBERGER
E. L. TATUM, *Editors*

Preface

Molecular biology is on the threshold of unique discovery, which in essence will require the discarding of worn-out concepts and the acquiring of new points of view. As applied to the field of membrane phenomena, Hechter in a recent discussion has pointed out succinctly the need for a new approach to biological membrane analysis: "Diverse disciplines and subdisciplines – each with its own concepts and techniques, concentrating on one aspect of membrane function or another – have contributed to our conceptual picture of cellular membranes in a voluminous literature, difficult to integrate and impossible to review. All of the diverse disciplines involved in the study of membranes use their own special language and basic assumptions, some of which are unstated. It is apparent that all could converge at the molecular level, making possible a universal language. The goal of molecular membranology should be to formulate a model of cell membranes in a unifying configuration especially satisfactory and meaningful to the biophysicist, physical chemist, biochemist and physiologist".

It is to this end that this book is written. No attempt has been made to review comprehensively all of the literature on the particular aspects of the membrane problem treated here. Rather, a selection has been made on the basis of relevance to the entire field and depth for the specialist. I have striven for clarity of language and breadth of application with emphasis on those references which will lead the reader to further sources. Seemingly unrelated areas (e.g. artificial perm-selective membranes) have been left too long unattended and in the pale of biological membrane research. It is hoped that the dipole membrane model presented here will stimulate further interest in the vast number of unanswered questions, as described in the introductory sections of this book, and aid in the solution to these problems.

The work on this dipole membrane model began in 1963 at the First Theoretical Biology Center, at the State University of New York at Buffalo, under Professor J. F. Danielli's direction with the assistance of Professor I. H. Shames, Chairman of the Department of Engineering Science and Interdisciplinary Studies. In 1965, the project was carried to the Neurobiology Division, Psychiatric Institute, University of Maryland School of Medicine, under Professor R. G. Grenell's direction where currently intensive investigations of applications to nerve membranes are being studied. Most of this work could not have been completed without the able assistance of two graduate students, Mr. Alan J. Blatt, and Mr. Vincent Gallucci. Further analyses similar to chapter 7 may be found in their Master's theses and chapter 7 represents only a very small part of their work. With the additional assistance of two technicians, Mr. Gary Russell and Mr. Rush Allen, the theory, calculations and computer programs for the entire project were checked and rechecked for errors. Special commendation goes to Mr. Blatt and Mr. Allen for their contributions to the mathematical analyses in chapters 6, 8, and 11.

A large measure of gratitude is extended to Professor L. Shohet of the University of Wisconsin, Department of Electrical Engineering, who assisted with the mathematics and theory in chapter 12. Finally, many thanks are expressed to my friend and colleague, Professor R. G. Grenell, who offered me the opportunity which has made this book possible.

Contents

SECTION III. APPLICATIONS OF A SURFACE DIPOLE MODEL TO
BIOLOGICAL CELLS

Introduction

This book represents a first attempt at considering a functional electrostatic model of biological membranes based on its structural constituents. Thus, the phospholipid bilayer is considered the basic building block of the biological membrane. By increasingly more complex electrostatic analyses of this phospholipid bilayer, and other constituents at the molecular level, it should be possible to determine its functional mechanisms.

Section I, chapter 1, reviews selectively current theories and knowledge bearing on the molecular structure and functions related to biological membranes. In this section, current methods utilizing electrostatic statistical theories are distinguished from the non-statistical approach described in detail in sections II and III.

Section II describes methods and calculations useful in describing a single phospholipid layer. Part A of this section is concerned with simple methods that are representative of first-order electric field and potential values from this layer. Although the derivations in chapters 2 and 3 involve only the axis of symmetry of a flat circular sheet, they are nonetheless useful for their simplicity and for a first approximation to field and potential effects. In a similar manner, chapter 4 shows how the axial symmetric cases of differing geometrically shaped linear and planar arrays of phospholipids, influence field and potential values. Although the models used in chapters 2–4 are far removed from the biological case, it will be shown in later chapters that their field and potential values are within an order of magnitude of more rigorously defined models simulating the biological membrane. Justification for including these models is made on the basis that they are most easily incorporated into the biological curriculum and may be utilized as an exercise in achieving more sophisticated theory described in part B of section II. Part B of section II is divided into three chapters. The first of these, chapter 5, deals with the force fields anywhere in the domain of a planar array of fixed dipoles or charges. Chapter 6 shows the influence upon the field of specific rotation properties of individual phospholipids. Utilizing cholesterol as the layer of phospholipid, chapter 7 describes the effect of an added protein coat and a large macromolecule in the domain.

Sections III brings the reader to the biological applications of this surface model. Chapter 8 shows that orientation effects of dipoles in a single layer, or the use of a double layer of dipoles comparable to the biological case, cause little change in the electric field intensity functions. Based on these proofs, a rationale is developed for utilizing a single layer of dipoles in a specific orientation as representative of the phospholipid bilayer biological case. Utilizing this representative model of oriented dipoles, chapter 9 describes the field and potential effects in a sphere of biological dimensions. Chapter 10 considers this same model for biological dimensions comparable to square and elongated parallelepipeds. In this chapter, it is noted that field effects divide up the cell into polarized compartments. Several other approaches, not included here, utilizing electrostatic theory, confirm that this phenomenon must occur. Chapter 11 offers a first attempt at considering the field effects inside a cylinder utilizing this dipole model. Although far removed from the biological characteristics of nerve conduction, it opens new possibilities for its mechanisms. Finally, chapter 12 reviews the concepts of bound water in biological membranes and points up the consequences of water structures based on this dipole theory.

Background for membrane structure and function

Chapter 1

Validity of a dipole model
for biological membranes

Contents

1 *Introduction*

Numerous structural models of biological membrane systems have been proposed to explain a wide variety of intra and extra cellular functions. Both "analog" and "molecular" models have been brought forward to explain phenomena dealing with motility, excitability, transport, permeability, adsorption, adhesion, and biochemical processes. Analog models (e.g., electrical circuitry, mechanical dashpots and springs, ion exchange columns etc.) have been useful in describing biologically functioning membranes as well as artificial membranes which possess one or more characteristics similar to the biological case. At this time, models of the molecular structure of biological membranes are necessarily based upon incomplete data at a macromolecular level and real structures, complex as they are, are often considered by making specific assumptions as to which variables may be neglected. In order to assess the validity of such treatments and to obtain a broad insight into the significant features of membrane structure and function, a brief review of artificial and biological membranes follows.

1.1 *Artificial membranes*

Within the past decade, by far the greater number of experimental membrane studies have centered around artificial perm-selective membranes [1-12]. These membranes vary from simple chemical ion-exchange columns [1] and specially prepared synthetic films [2-9], to specific artificially prepared membranes of biological lipid origin [10]. The basic principles arising out of these studies involve the elucidation of structure necessary to perform a given chemical selective function. Thus, numerous studies by DeKorosy and others [2,4] have indicated various chemical structures that will selectively pass sulfate, chloride, sodium and potassium ions, to name only a few. Investigations have included a variety of cellulose membranes along with their electron micrographs [5,8,9], *liquid* anionic and cationic exchange membranes of a variety of organic structures [3], polyvinyl alcohol and derivative membranes along with their electron micrographs [7], and polystyrene membranes [11].

The methods used to study these membranes vary from simple temperature dependence considerations [12] through classical electrical measurements involving capacitance, resistance and potential [7]), to more elaborate studies involving electro-osmosis and permeation of water vapor [6,9]). The theory applied to these experimental findings most often involves thermodynamic and kinetic treatments to derive permeability, reflection and frictional coefficients [5,11]). Analysis often involves applications of "double layer" theory [13]).

A most successful approach has been to fill millipore filters, of known dimensions and flow properties, with non-aqueous solutions of phospholipid. Analysis of their electrical properties in electrolyte solutions has uncovered the functional role of specific phospholipids in ion exchange mechanisms [10]). Although structurally dissimilar to biological membranes such studies uncover the possible roles played by individual chemical constituents in the biological case.

More theoretical emphasis has been given to artificial membranes by considering the adsorption isotherms associated with a large number of surface phenomena [14-16]). Often biologically unrelated theoretical studies can be applied to yield useful information. Numerous examples [17-19]) may be found in the literature where desorption and adsorption of thin organic films of diverse macromolecular structure on metal surfaces have been investigated. Studies of coacervation [20]) may also pertain. Perhaps of more direct interest are those works concerned with adsorption isotherms of the Langmuir type or B.A.T. theory, where flocculation, dispersion, mobility, molecular size and surface area are variables [15,16,21]). An excellent review is given by Kipling [14]).

The electrostatics of adsorption has been sparsely treated focussing only upon specific geometries and special systems [22,23]). A review of the additivity of intermolecular forces at interfaces is given by Fowkes [24]). The analysis of these systems classically involves double layer theory and van der Waal's interactions.

Recent interest in the role of metal ions binding to artificial membraneous structures and lipid constituents has given new emphasis to complex formation in membrane structure and function [25]). Binding and complexing properties of calcium, magnesium and heavier metals with membraneous materials and lipid fractions of brain tissue have only recently been investigated [26]).

1.2 *Biological membranes*

1.2.1 FUNCTIONAL ASPECTS

Functional analogs of transport phenomena for biological membranes have been well characterized in the literature for some time [27]). Ion transport, in particular, has received much attention usually without reference to structural features of a membrane model [28, 29]). Thus, diffusion equations, conservation of charge, and net flux equations are the basis of such analyses. Recently, attention has been given to problems of permeability and excitability in terms of analog models based on membranes of limited structural identity [30, 31]). Of special note is the work of Rudin and Mueller [32]) with artificial membranes which parallel known biological structures that have been reconstituted from lipid materials. A model to explain induced excitability based on such artificial membranes is given in terms of electronic semiconductor tunnel diodes. This model describes the transition kinetics of "active" membranes almost entirely in terms of electronic circuitry.

   More classical approaches using experimental data on the erythrocyte membrane have suggested models accounting for mechanical properties. These models range from springs and dashpots (also based on monolayer studies) to mathematical models of elasticity and strain [33]). The latter have been useful in calculating "membrane tension".

   It is of interest to consider those models utilizing a statistical mechanical treatment of permeability of electrolytes and non-electrolytes through biological membranes. The starting point of the analysis is usually the statistical mechanical expression for the mean force and frictional coefficient of a molecule of a given species following the mathematical procedures of Katchalsky, now classical in this field. Making use of the concepts of electroneutrality, vanishing net electric current density and equations of conservation, expressions for permeability and reflection coefficients are derived in terms of concentrations and electric potential. The only assumptions necessary to the model are differences in electro-chemical potential across the membrane and the presence of non-ionizable or ionizable groups and co-ions in the system. Thus, these models are independent of most structural features being solely based on the functional aspects of the transport process. This is most desirable if the origin of the variables described can ultimately fit into the framework of the known molecular configurations in the bio-logical membrane. Unfortunately present concepts describing permea-bility fail in this regard. Frictional and permeability coefficients, osmotic pressure and volume flow to name only a few, are concepts derived from macroscopic variables. Although extrapolation to the molecular level is possible through statistical mechanics, the usefulness of these concepts in analyzing the functioning of structural components at the molecular level, where individual non-statistical interactions are of such importance (see § 2), has not been demonstrated.

1.2.2 STRUCTURAL ASPECTS

Evidence which has been accumulated from a diversity of sources for a limiting biological membrane composed of a protein-coated bimolecular layer of lipid and phospholipid, has created a framework for membrane structure to which most agree. In addition, there is general agreement that the membrane is roughly 100 to 1000 Å thick and that the lipid bilayer is 20–100 Å thick. There is also general qualitative agreement that the bilayer contains cholesterol, galactosides and phospholipids of which sphingomyelin, phosphatidylethanolamine, phosphatidylcholine, phos-phatidylserine, diphosphoglyceroinositide are the major components. The hydrocarbon chains are directed toward the interior of the bilayer and the polar groups are exposed on both sides in contact with the protein. It has been recently pointed out [34] that little is known of the protein structure (whether monolayer or otherwise) although such studies are currently in progress [35].

With this very simple picture of membrane structure in mind, it is necessary to consider in more detail the evidence for:
(a) Limitations of fine structure; dimensions of the bilayer
(b) Molecular constituents and packing of the bilayer
(c) Orientation of lipid molecules in the bilayer.

(a) *Limitations of fine structure; dimensions of the bilayer*

Studies by electron microscopy of both organelle and plasma membranes have been adequately reviewed elsewhere [36]. Two points of view are current: (1) a static structure of the bilayer of finite dimensions with adsorbed protein layers and (2) a dynamic picture of the bilayer in which more than one structure of "folding" and "unfolding" is involved. The first approach assumes that the osmium tetroxide and potassium permanganate fixed films yield a picture of membrane structure dependent on care in preparation of films and optical resolution. Electron microscope photographs by numerous investigators (e.g. Stoeckenius [37]), Elliot [38a]), Robertson [38b]), etc.) appear quite definitive. However, differences in fixation technique have been studied by electrophoresis and point up marked differences in information obtained [39]). From such studies, the chemical constituent of the red blood cell membrane responsible for its charge characteristics has been identified.

The second approach assumes that discrepancies in calculating dimensions from electron micrographs represent different phases of a dynamic membrane structure [40]). Evidence of differences in dimensions of the bilayer has been brought together to re-enforce this point of view. Yet, proof of exact dimensions within the 20–100 Å dimension for the bilayer by either the static or dynamic approach is still lacking. It is of interest to the biologist to learn that within a few years the electron microscopist expects to obtain ultra-high magnification to a resolution of 2 Å [41]).

Unique studies based on electron microscopy of membraneous structures, involves "mapping" of membranes and components of cells from such photographs. Thus, diagrams illustrating the reconstruction of membraneous sections [42]) open up a new approach to analyzing dimensions of the membrane. The relationship of this point of view to "electrostatic mapping" of membraneous structures is given in chapters 5 and 10. Suffice it to say here that enough is now known of cytochemical activities of a cell relative to membraneous structures that a topographical distribution of enzymic activities in different cellular components has been attempted [43]). Mapping of structures from electromicrographs of nucleoli [44]) and mitochondria [45]) are well known. Other structures have also been mapped [38]). The current point of view is that the membraneous structures are continuous throughout the entire cell [43]).

Much attention has been given in permeability studies to the size of pores in membraneous structures. An excellent review of this topic has recently been published [46]). The pore size of the red blood cell membrane has been evaluated by several investigators to be 4 Å. This is well below the resolution of electron microscopy and must therefore await further technological advances for confirmation.

Within the past few years, much interest has been shown in "black film" formation by soaps and lipid materials. Studies by Rudin and Mueller [47]), Overbeek [48]), Thompson [49]), and Haydon [50]) (to name only a few) have shown that these artificial bilayer films are comparable in dimensions and electrical properties to the range of dimensions and properties of their biological counterparts. Although a similar variation in the width of the bilayer is reported from one investigator to another as in the biological case, well substantiated evidence has been gathered of the packing of molecules in these artificial bilayers. Thus, the hydrocarbon chains are considered perpendicular to the plane of the membrane, while the polar groups have freedom of orientation with external fields depending on molecular packing. The density is firmly fixed between 20–30 Å^2 per chain. The average packing area per polar group is given as 25 Å^2.

Since permeability and electrical properties are so similar to the biological case, much information of the chemical constituents and structure of the bilayer may be gathered from these investigations of black films. Further reference to these studies will be made throughout this chapter.

(b) *Molecular constituents and packing of the bilayer*

Much interest has recently been manifested in enzymes and "receptor" molecules associated with the protein layers of membraneous structures. Thus, the relation of cytochrome enzymes to mitochondrial membranes, and adrenergic and cholinergic receptors of the plasma membrane of nerve endings are being intensively studied. However, these moieties are found only in cells and organelles of specialized function thus limiting their usefulness to a generalized model of membrane structure. It is necessary then to confine this review to those features immediately pertinent to the *lipid* bilayer of all cells.

A number of studies have identified enzyme constituents associated with the biosynthesis of bilayer constituents. Thus, Brodie et al. [51]) have isolated the enzyme-bound intermediates in the biosynthesis of mevalonic and palmitic acids. They have also indicated the route for the biosynthesis of cholesterol. In a similar manner, Rothfield et al. [52]) have studied the lipid composition of the cell envelope as it relates to enzyme components for the biosynthesis of bacterial lipo-polysaccharide in the cell wall. Investigations of the lysosomal membrane indicate that this bilayer has the characteristics of a charged membrane [53]). Also included in the above study is an excellent review of the functions of various kinds of membranes of the cell.

Analytical techniques for the determination and identification of specific lipids from membraneous structures have developed to a point comparable with other biological components. Use of gel-filtration as a means of separating polar and non-polar fractions from lipid mixtures has been highly successful, as well as chromatographic separations with 100 % recovery and identification of components [54]). Contamination of lipid extracts has always been a major problem and has now been success-fully resolved by use of specially prepared sephadex columns [55]). This method is rapid and highly effective for the removal of non-lipid contam-inants with no serious loss of lipid.

Numerous studies have been concerned with the identification and elucidation of specific structures of complex lipids and phospholipids from biological sources [56, 57]). Although these studies do not directly relate to the components of the bilayer, their usefulness in understanding the constituents of lipid structures may ultimately apply to the membrane. Thus, studies of patients with hyperlipidemia [58]) may in time become of great value in analyzing structural defects in membraneous systems.

Of special note are studies of the liquid-crystalline nature of phospho-lipids and cholesterol [59]). Infrared spectra indicate that the unit mem-brane exists rather critically on the border line of a phase transition between liquid and condensed phases. This is consistent with data of packing density of artificial black bilayers. Infrared spectra also indicate the importance of cis and trans configurations of phospholipid molecules.

Specific analyses of lipid components of membraneous structures are most often performed on erythrocyte and macrophage mem-branes [57, 60-62]). Labeling techniques are now common and yield data of the per cent lipid component in the bilayer [60]). Separation and quan-titative determination of phosphorylated intermediates from the red blood cell membrane have been analyzed by high voltage electro-phoresis [61]). Fluorescent labels have been used in isolating and identi-fying components of the plasma membrane [63]). It has been shown that the cholesterol-phospholipid ratio from lipids of butanol-treated erythro-cytes is significant in relation to permeability [64]). The chemical composi-tion of the plasma membrane relative the chemical composition of the whole cell has also been studied at some length [65]). Investigations of micelle formation of lipids and related substances cannot be overlooked in understanding the stability and formation of the bilayer relative its chemical composition. Studies in polar and non-polar solvents with micelles of lecithin indicate dimensions of interacting head groups and conversions of monomolecular leaflets to the bimolecular type [66]. The relationship of the dielectric constant of these micelle groups to permeability is also analyzed. The use of anionic, cationic and non-ionic detergents in micelle formation, yields data on the limiting sizes of aggregates relative their charge properties [67-69]. By examination of spontaneous binding of protein from mitochondria with micellar phospholipids a possible mechanism of genesis of bilayers in the cell [70] can be inferred.

The *packing* of chemical constituents in the bilayer of biological membranes has been sparsely considered. Research concerned with molecular sieving by cell membranes of *Bacillus megaterium* indicates a hexagonal arrangement in the ultrastructure of lipid bilayers [71]. However, evidence is still to scant for any definitive conclusions and packing in crystals from models must still be used as a guide [72]. Data that is also helpful from monolayer studies will be described later in this chapter. The use of the computer to derive theoretically packing structures must not be overlooked. Analogs of chemical models can be built by the computer by actually calculating the combinations of many discrete atomic coordinates for a given membrane configuration. Quantitative constraints can be placed on the system and structures consistent with these searched out [73].

(c) *Orientation of lipid molecules in the bilayer as they relate to membrane function*

Early surface chemical studies on monolayers of lipid substances at air–water and oil–water interfaces (1925–1940) elucidated the basic structural orientation of molecules in liquid and condensed phases. Potential measurements, although crude and often contradictory in those early investigations, sustained a picture of lipid molecules in which the hydrocarbon tails are perpendicular to the plane of the water molecules in a condensed phase, and slightly tilted in a liquid phase. Many of these force–area and potential–area curve measurements are still useful today. An excellent review of surface chemical studies on monolayers is given by Davies and Rideal [74]. It has been shown from these early studies that the larger the area per molecule the flatter it lies in the plane. Changes in the potential during this tilting process indicate a change in the orientation of the polar end group which has been theoretically substantiated by analysis of the orientation angle of the dipole moment. A similar effect was obtained by changing the concentration of electrolyte in the aqueous solution. On comparing bilayer and monolayer molecular densities the usefulness of this data becomes apparent. Thus, with molecules packed on 25 $Å^2$ squares per carbon chain, bordering on a transition between liquid and condensed phases, the polar groups and/or their hydrocarbon chains, on strictly geometric grounds, have sufficient room to tilt in aligning with an external field.

In turning to more recent monolayer studies with both ionized and dipole polar end groups, depth of immersion of the head group into the aqueous phase has been established [75]. However, interest in the orientation of the polar group has not appeared. The influence of charged polar groups of monolayers on protein molecules has also been investigated [76,77]. In general, recent references ignore the influence of the dipole end groups of lipid molecules as being an insignificant and negligible factor in electrostatic calculations [22,23,78]. It will be shown in the following sections that this is an incorrect assumption. Much research on transmembrane potentials in living biological membranes attempts to explain the data solely in terms of ionic concentrations within the cell or vacuole [79-88]. Equally incorrect are molecular models of the membrane which treat theoretically the protein layer as the only significant electrostatic component [111].

The influence of external electric fields on the bilayer structure has not been experimentally established. Preliminary reports on the effects of electric fields on mice and erythrocytes [89,90] are of interest. Studies of the application of uniform and non-uniform fields on organic liquids show unexpected results but are far removed from membrane structure [91].

A number of structural models, which in some ways are related to the bilayer structure, have been proposed to explain special functions. Daniel [92-94] analyzes the high electric field intensity properties of linear chains of dipoles of solid secondary alcohol from a statistical mechanical point of view. From this analysis, dielectric saturation in chains of hydrogen bonds is used as a model for field controlled ion trapping in a mechanism of nerve membranes. The model consists of a pyramid of molecular size whose sides are highly polarizable chains of dipoles, such as occur in solid long chain alcohols and which may be comparable to bilayer constituents. It is postulated that the apex of the pyramid controls the electric potential of a pore which is capable of trapping sodium ions.

A model of dipole orientation and polarization is presented in a theory of dielectric crystalline dispersion by Yamafugi [95]. The dielectric dispersion of the polymer is explained on the basis of dipole reorientation accompanied with segmental micro-Brownian motion of the polymer, called "local relaxation modes". Although far removed from bilayer structure, it is of interest to note that even in solid macromolecular crystallites, reorientation of dipoles plays a major role in field effects.

In analyzing the adhesiveness of leukocytes, a model based on a membrane of local protuberances is proposed by Bongham [96]. The derivation is based on a small radius of curvature enabling close approach at ordinary thermal energies of the London–van der Waals attractions and repulsions of electrostatic charges. The treatment is by statistical mechanics and the structural features of the bilayer are neglected.

A mechanism of cellular and subcellular motility has been set forth to represent a model based on the bilayer structure [97]. This model is mechanical in nature, and ignores electrostatic effects.

One of the most noteworthy and comprehensive representations of the biological membrane has been set forth by Hechter [111]. His theoretical considerations, at the molecular level, of the water molecules in and around the bilayer, as well as his analysis of configurations and packing of the protein monolayer, yield by far the most penetrating insight into membrane structure. His investigation of hexagonal and clathrate structures (ice-like structures) of water coupled with hexagonal and pentahedral configurations in the packing of the protein monolayer is marshalled with much theoretical and experimental evidence. The influence of the bilayer itself as it interacts at the molecular level with this "hexagonal subunit model" of water and protein is yet to be determined. Sterically, the two models are compatible. This study also proposes the concept of "transducing units" in the bilayer structure. These units are considered to be ordered macromolecular assemblies, which involve enzymes and other macromolecules coupled energy wise and spatially. Functionally they are assumed to assist the transport of ions and other solutes in contraction and in other active membrane processes. However, most of the model data for the bilayer are taken from studies of mitochondria [112]). As yet, there is insufficient evidence to assume the hexagonal packing in the bilayer which is inferred in this "transducer" model.

A model taking into account orientation effects of dipoles in the polar end groups of the bilayer is proposed by Goldman [98]). He presents a molecular structural basis for the excitation properties of axons. His structural model consists of a double layer of lipid and phospholipids which change their orientation and combining properties under the influence of an electric field. The driving forces are assumed to be electrostatic forces and concentration gradients. The electrostatics is treated from the point of view of statistical mechanics with structural models of the phospholipids. Justification of the dipole orientation is given in terms of the atomic configuration of the polar end groups of the complex phospholipids.

It is the purpose of the remaining sections of this chapter to show that if a bilayer structure of the membrane is assumed not only in specialized nerve cells of the Goldman model, but with *all* membraneous structures the dipoles of the polar end groups yield significantly high fields comparable to an array of full electronic charges. It will be shown that the potential energy from a dipole layer is four to five orders of magnitude greater than kT at distances between 100 and 1000 Å away from the membrane. The necessity for a non-statistical approach to these calculations will be explained and illustrated. Thus the purpose here is to describe a simple comprehensive non-statistical electrostatic structural theory of the bilayer pertaining to all cells with applications in many areas related to membrane function.

2 *A non-statistical approach*

It has been established by several investigators [99-101]) that many of the smallest biological systems known, including PPLO's (pleuro pneumonia-like organisms) and small bacteria contain as few as 1–3 macromolecules of any one kind per cell depending upon the classification of size of macromolecules. This result has been established by considering the total mass (or weight) of a cell, its total volume, and the number of independent enzyme functions which it must perform to maintain life. Thus, with an average molecular weight for each necessary enzyme, it is possible to estimate the number of different macromolecules present in PPLO. It can be shown [102–103]) by the above methods that 100 macromolecules would be a high value. A sample calculation follows:

Weight of smallest organisms and PPLO $= 1$–30 Md* (Md $= 10^{-17}$ g)

100 macromolecules, each of molecular weight of 1000:

$$(10^6 \text{ a.u.})(10^{-23}) = 10^{-17} \text{ g} = 1 \text{ Md.}$$

These facts indicate that the usefulness of statistical theory in examining these smallest living systems is limited. Although the statistical treatment of small numbers allows a rigorous treatment of small groups of entities with identical characteristics, it is inapplicable to a system composed entirely of distinct entities of widely varying characteristics. In a similar manner, an electrostatics treatment based upon statistics of time independent functions is also of little help. Most statistical analyses of time independent functions are based on Boltzmann distributions. Where the number of identifiable and distinct macromolecules is markedly small, such that no more than three of any one kind are present (e.g., with PPLO) Boltzmann statistical theory breaks down.

One must not infer from the above facts that for larger biological cells statistical theory is equally invalid. On the contrary, the number of identical enzymes and macromolecules increases with the size of the cell. The purpose here is to indicate the usefulness of the discrete approach, where statistical theory fails. In turn, the study of discrete field theory may also yield information regarding larger cells. It is to be noted that in human physiology it is quite common for substances to have activity in the ppm (parts per million) concentration range [104]). Much of receptor site theory is based upon single molecules acting on a given structure. In addition, in order for a given structure in a cell to replicate it must attract molecules from a distance (arbitrarily chosen as greater than 100 Å), select the proper molecules, and order them into the proper array. Complexity and specificity of biological structures as a general phenomenon demands the ordering of single molecules out of an array. Such selectivity, in its broadest sense, is difficult to conceive by statistical theory.

* Pirie (1964)

Another impediment in dealing with molecular structure at the *micro-scopic* level involves the use of variables based on *macroscopic* concepts. Thus, viscosity or frictional coefficients (to name only two) are based upon continuum macroscopic phenomena. Although the viscosity or frictional coefficient of a single molecule may be a useful extrapolation in manipulating measurements, its meaning in describing the interactions of individual molecules at the microscopic level is suspect. (One does not speak of the viscosity of a single molecule.) Thus, the non-statistical or discrete approach to describe the electric field intensity and potential energy functions of a single molecule or, the sum of such functions for an array of discrete molecules, has very real meaning at the microscopic level.

Although the mathematics and physics of such a non-statistical approach for field and potential theory has been available for some time, its usefulness has been previously relegated to electrical phenomena of non-conducting systems of metals [105]). With the inception of inter-disciplinary points of view it is possible to consider a model of the lipid portion of biological membranes as a bilayer of fixed dipoles which are arranged perpendicular to the plane.

A further deterrent in the application of this theory has been the comparison of force fields of a single electronic charge and dipole. The comparison of functions of $1/r^2$ and $1/r^3$ has led investigators to discount dipole interactions as being negligible. In §4 it will be shown that for *arrays* of dipoles these fields are comparable to a sheet of electronic charges.

With the advent of computer techniques it is now convenient to sum up the discrete field effects from large distributions of fixed charges and dipoles. By computer methods difficult solutions to "discrete sum" or "integral equations" of large charge distributions may easily be obtained.

It is of interest to compare this non-statistical field approach to double layer theory. The original Gouy–Chapman equations are based on a fixed charged surface with an opposing layer of mobile ions of opposite sign distributed some distance away. The statistical analysis of this system, which is applicable to many electrolyte solutions of colloidal particles, "locks" into the mathematics the true field values of the fixed charged surface. Thus, the usefulness of double layer theory is restricted to systems where statistical numbers of mobile ions are of major importance. Where the emphasis is upon the fixed charge or dipole structure and ordering and selection of single macromolecules are involved, true field values are required.

3 *Assumptions of a dipole model*

Any structural model used to explain biological membrane phenomena must satisfy, in the first instance, the molecular configuration of the bilayer as described in § 1. If the framework of all biological membranes is a bimolecular lipid leaflet of 20–100 Å across, then a "molecular model" is defined which represents in a "chemical" sense the real lipid and phospholipid molecules found in the actual configuration of the bilayer. For this model to be valid it must also include water molecules and electrolyte, which are always present, as well as macromolecules of protein adjacent to both sides of the bilayer [111]). Since at this time, these entities are structurally uncertain at the molecular level, it is not possible to identify these variables in any great detail.

From the "molecular model" it is necessary to abstract electrostatic properties of first order effect that will constitute an "electrostatic" or "physical" model. Thus, initial analyses will neglect the hydrocarbon chains in the bilayer which give rise to London–van der Waals dispersion forces which vary as $1/r^7$. Charge and dipole effects which vary as $1/r^2$ and $1/r^3$ must be taken into account. Therefore, the "physical model" of the bilayer will consist of a double layer of discrete dipoles, whose actual dimensions and dipole moments are taken from the real lipid molecules of the "molecular model" (see fig. 1). Since the bilayer often contains a net negative charge, due to partitioning of electrolyte or ionization of polar groups, a fixed charged density may also be superimposed.

A further abstraction of the "physical model" is possible which will substantially simplify the electrostatics calculations. The *discrete* dipoles and charges may be idealized to *point* dipoles and charges which maintain their charge density but are dimensionless. Equations utilizing such point functions are quite common to electrostatics and are valid at distances greater than the charge separation in the discrete case.

Calculations of the electric field intensity and potential energy of the bilayer adjacent to, and on the membrane, may be performed for any one of the three models presented. The inherent difficulties of working with the "molecular model" are overcome by treating the "discrete physical model" or "*idealized*" case. This is valid as long as the *correspondence* between models is carefully analyzed and limitations recognized.

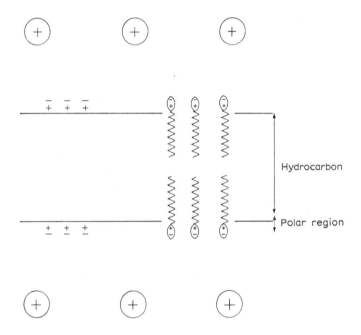

Fig. 1. Dipole representation of bilayer structure of biological membrane

In considering first order effects, since the field and potential functions are very much dependent upon the orientation of the dipoles, it is necessary to consider a configuration consistent with the model which will yield *maximum* values of these functions. Such an analysis will yield the *upper limits to* the field and potential energy of the membrane. Further refinements taking into account second order effects and different configurations will be bounded by this upper limit. Since it is known that protein molecules and electrolyte exist on both sides of the bilayer it is assumed that centers of large charge density exist adjacent to the membrane. In the first instance the magnitudes of these charge centers are unspecified but are assumed to be large enough to cause the dipoles in the layer adjacent to it, to be oriented towards the charge center. Assuming that the dipoles thus align themselves into the field of a charge center adjacent to each layer, it is possible to calculate the *maximum* field and potential energy of a sheet of such dipoles. Since many of the dipoles in the "molecular model" will have different rotation properties (cholesterol, esters and phospholipids) in order to consider the maximum effect (or upper limit) it is assumed that these dipoles all have free rotation. Further refinements will add restraints to the system, taking into account the molecular species involved.

It has been well established [106] that the stability of the bilayer resides in the attractive forces (van der Waals–London dispersion forces) of the hydrocarbon chains as opposed to the repulsive forces of the two extreme layers of dipoles. Experimental data leading to these facts have been gained from studies of lipid micelles and early investigations of Debye [107]). Thus, the hydrocarbon chains "screen out" the effect of the charge centers beneath the bilayer so that only one layer of dipoles need be considered. With this simplifying assumption the alignment of dipoles to a point beneath the array will yield *maximum* field and potential energy values from the membrane. In the limiting case a maximum dielectric constant of 80 may be utilized to take into account the screening effect of the aqueous phase. However, use of a dielectric constant is inconsistent with this non-statistical approach. At the molecular level the dielectric of a single water molecule has no meaning. Thus, a true evaluation of the field effects of the water molecules interacting with the dipole layer must be demonstrated by similar methods. Until this has been completed, an upper limit using a dielectric constant of 80 must suffice.

It is of interest to consider the various configurations that dipoles may take in a single layer of the "physical model". Evidence from numerous sources (see § 1) points to the fact that the lipid molecules are perpendicular to the sheet or slightly tilted. Thus, the polar groups may be perpendicular or may rotate into an external field depending on constraints. It will be pointed out in § 4 that these two configurations yield potential energy values which are four to five orders of magnitude greater than kT (kT being the classical evaluation of the random thermal energy) at distances 100 to 1000 Å away from the sheet. In a similar manner if the dipoles lie flat on the sheet, tail to tail (a configuration unlikely in the biological case) similarly high potential values are found at large distances from the sheet. Analyses of fixed charged sheets comparable to the dipole sheets indicate values that are similar or no more than one to two orders of magnitude greater than the dipole sheet. Thus it can be shown from purely non-statistical electrostatic considerations that a dipole layer with *any* uniform configuration or orientation has comparable field and potential energy values to a charge sheet and that these values are remarkably high.

The calculations for this non-statistical evaluation of the field and potential energy of a dipole and charge sheet may be performed in several ways. The simplest method is to assume a uniform fixed-point dipole moment density or fixed-point charge density on a circular flat sheet and by integration procedures to calculate the field and potential energy on the axis of symmetry assuming the dipoles are perpendicular or have aligned to a point on this axis. The derivations and analyses of such electric field and potential energy functions are treated in chapter 2 and 3. Since the dipole moments and dimensions of the discrete dipoles of the lipid molecules of the various chemical species concerned are quite similar, average values have been chosen to be representative of the membrane. Using an integration procedure, values at some distance from the sheet as a function of its radius, can be obtained. This first approximation indicates an order of maximum effect of the dipole or charge layer. The influence of geometry has also been studied and is given in chapter 4. Similar derivations giving the entire field off the axis of symmetry are given in chapter 5. In chapter 6 the discrete approach is used by summing field effects of discrete dipoles. It is shown that the result by discrete summation is identical in almost all respects to that obtained by integration methods. Chapter 6 also analyzes the rotation properties of lipid molecules and how the mathematics of this method is influenced by such properties. With the discrete approach, field values are also calculated *on* the sheet. The dipole moments were obtained from pure substances in the gaseous or liquid phases.

The above calculations are performed by assuming, in the flat circular distributions, a point charge or dipole density of $q/25$ Å^2 and $p/25$ Å^2. During the integration procedures the density functions are "smeared" over the surface and summed. For the computer summation and discrete cases, square sheets were utilized of area equal to the circular sheets in order to compare results. Point and discrete charges and dipoles were fixed in 5 Å by 5 Å squares in a grid over the surface. The computer summations were carried out maintaining the fixed charge and dipole grid array. A radial distribution of equal area per charge or dipole upon a flat circular sheet has also been analyzed. Field values on and off the sheet are comparable to those of the square grid (see fig. 2).

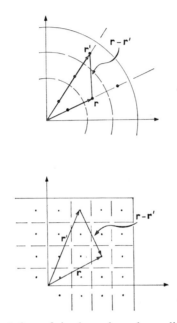

Fig. 2. Representations of circular and equal area dipole distributions

4 *Results*

The electric field intensity E on the axis of symmetry of a flat circular sheet of focussed point dipoles and charges, is graphed as a function of z, the distance from the sheet and R, the radius of the sheet in figs. 3a and 3b resp. Using a point dipole density of $4.2 \times 10^{-28}/(25 \text{ Å}^2)$ and a point charge density of $1.6 \times 10^{-19}/(25 \text{ Å}^2)$, consistent with black lipid film measurements, the summed force fields of the oriented dipoles are larger than those of comparable fixed charged sheets at $z = 1\text{–}25 \text{ Å}$. At greater distances the force field of the dipole sheet drops off at a faster rate than that of the charge sheet but still yields remarkably high force fields for

$z = 100$–1000 Å. A complete derivation and discussion of results is given in chapter 2. The graphs of field equations for the axis of symmetry corresponding to the dipoles perpendicular to the sheet and lying flat on the sheet, are given in figs. 4 and 5 resp. These graphs indicate that very large field values exist at relatively large distances (>100 Å) from the sheet corresponding to any *uniform* orientation of dipoles. Further, that

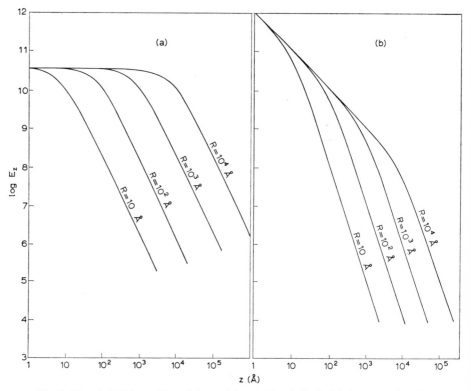

Fig. 3. Electric field intensities of charge (a) and aligned dipole (b) sheets as a function of distance z and radius of the sheet R

these fields are comparable to field values from sheets of fixed charge distributions.

In a similar manner, utilizing the same idealized point charge and dipole model, the potential energy is graphed as a function of z and R in fig. 6. For comparison purposes the plot for a point dipole and point charge as well as the value of kT (300 °K) is drawn in the figure. It is observed that the dipole sheet values are three to four orders of magnitude greater than kT at distances greater than 100 Å. The corresponding charged sheet values are another one to two orders of magnitude larger. Assuming a maximum screening effect of the water molecules in the adjacent media of one to two orders of magnitude (which would corre-

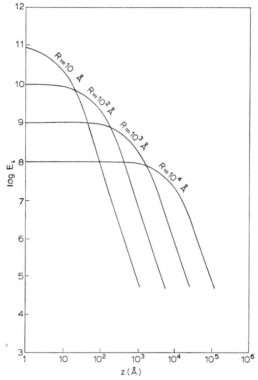

Fig. 4. Electric field intensities of non-aligned dipole sheets (dipoles perpendicular to the sheet) as a function of distance z and radius of the sheet R

spond to a dielectric constant of 80) the potential energy values on the axis of symmetry for the dipole sheet for any of the three orientations of dipoles (figs. 7, 8) is still remarkably large. Full derivation of equations for the potential energy and a discussion of results is given in chapter 3.

The influence of the geometry of the sheet on the field and potential energy functions is discussed in chapter 4. Equations are derived for the field and potential energy functions on the axis of symmetry for square, hemispherical, circular and infinite sheets and rods of fixed dipoles (aligned to an external field) and fixed charges. It is shown that the geometry of the sheet influences the field and potential in specific ways with comparable high field and potential energy values at large distances.

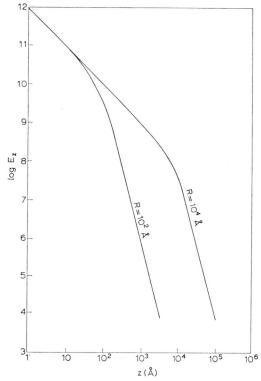

Fig. 5. Electric field intensities of non-aligned dipole sheets (dipoles lying in the plane of the sheet) as a function of distance z and radius of the sheet R

The off-axis derivations, using the same model and summing up the field by integral methods, are given in chapter 5. Similarly, high field values are found anywhere under the sheet as well as on the axis of symmetry. Contour maps of equipotential or isopotential surfaces have been included in chapter 5 to show the high force fields over the entire domain.

The mapping of cells or subcellular structures by electrostatics can be an extension of this point of view. A number of interesting phenomena arise out of such analyses due to unsymmetrical cancellations of field. Among them is the fact that normally the field drops off as one goes further away from the sheet. But in certain non-axial positions, the field starts low at

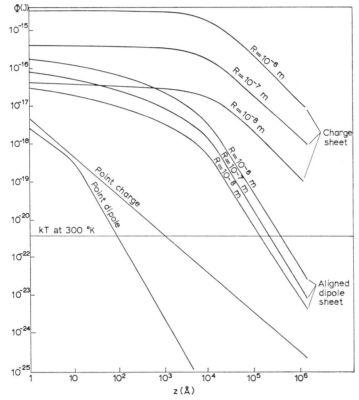

Fig. 6. Potential energy of charge and aligned dipole sheets as a function of distance z and radius of the sheet R

the sheet, builds up to a maximum at some distance away and then decreases in the normal fashion.

Justification for the use of the integration procedures (which in essence smears out the point charge or point dipole density over the sheet in summing up the field) is presented in chapter 6 which utilizes a discrete dipole approach. In these derivations discrete summation procedures are utilized by the computer to sum the fields of each individual dipole fixed in the array. Three types of rotation properties of dipoles are considered and compared. Although the dimensions and moments of real dipoles in the polar end groups of lipid molecules will vary through a small range

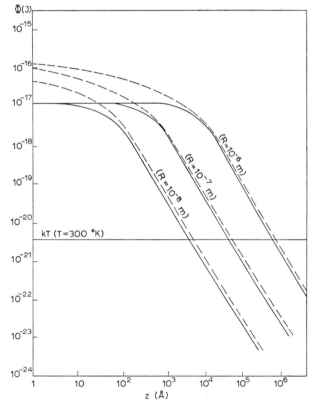

Fig. 7. Potential energy of non-aligned dipole sheets (dipoles perpendicular to the sheet) as a function of distance z and radius of the sheet R

of values, the invariant properties of their rotation characteristics are set forth in these derivations. Representative values for the length of the dipole and dipole moment were chosen. The comparisons indicate that the integration procedures are 99.999 % accurate up to 7 Å from the sheet. For accurate values closer to the sheet point functions must be discarded for discrete functions (dipoles with exact charge separation) and computer addition substituted for integral closed form solutions to field equations. These mathematical analyses also show that the discrete dipole case must be used in a nearest neighbor approximation to deter-

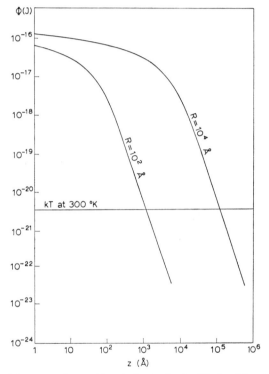

Fig. 8. Potential energy of non-aligned dipole sheets (dipoles lying in the plane of the sheet) as a function of distance z and radius of the sheet R

mine the fields *on* the sheet. These calculations (*on* the sheet) were performed for small arrays and indicate a gradient of 10^7 V/cm. This value is in line with the high field values suspected in the bilayer [108]) and theoretically derived in chapter 5. Refinements are still of course necessary to take into account second order effects of water molecules, electrolyte, and molecular constraints, both on and off the sheet.

The equations graphed in figs. 3–8 are summarized in §7 of chapter 4.

5 *Applications*

Although knowledge of the molecular structure of the biological membrane and the bilayer in particular, is incomplete, methods for calculating a wide range of biological phenomena from such data must be developed. The models and most of the procedures suggested in §§3 and 4 are relatively simple. However, these methods have been applied in large measure to the "idealized physical model". When considering more of the detail of the "molecular model", correspondence to the physical model may necessitate more sophisticated procedures. The purpose of this section is to point up various approaches to utilize the models suggested in tieing detailed molecular structure to biological functions.

As an extension of the methods proposed in chapters 1–6, self-consistent field studies have been completed for a sphere and flat sheet of homogeneous molecular dipoles with charge centers distributed beneath the layer. The electric field intensity is calculated at any point *on* the sheet taking into account interdipole fields due to reorientation of the dipoles. The high field values of the order of magnitude of 10^9 newton/coulomb in the bilayer may serve to explain the origin of electrostatic forces necessary to form pore structures and concentration gradients of ions. Thus, permeability coefficients in statistical theory may actually represent the symmetrical contributions of the electric field from the specific polar groups of the bilayer.

The treatment of the non-homogeneous dipole distribution on the basis of lipid analysis of membraneous structures (see §1) requires (1) careful interpretation of the polar end groups, (2) rotation and packing of the different kinds of lipids in the membrane. The latter is now undergoing intensive theoretical analysis. Thus, various ratios of phospholipid to cholesterol distributed in different ways in the membrane, may alter the field and potential functions on the membrane. Although dipole arrays yield relatively large force fields at large distances from the sheet, these forces are non-specific. By this is meant that the total electric field is made up of a sum of E_x, E_y and E_z components. In chapter 5 it is shown that only the E_z component is large at large distances and that the other components do not play a major role until distances less than 100 Å. Thus, a basis can be established for the ordering and selecting of macromolecules at close distances dependent upon the ordered characteristics of the different kinds of dipoles in the layer. The implications of this type of analysis for genesis of membraneous structures is evident.

The analysis given in chapter 5 indicates that points of high field intensity at points of symmetry occur at various locations under the sheet. These points of high field intensity would move if any type of motion were imparted to the membrane. Thus, a vibrating membrane would move the points of symmetry in a regular manner. An analysis of this type might very well serve as one mode of a replication mechanism of membrane structure. Much data is available in the literature to indicate that membraneous structures are often spaced with exacting regularity to each other. Evidence for the spacing between cells has recently been reviewed [109]) and indicates that the 175–200 Å spacing is found with regularity among most cells. Exceptions are to be found such as brain tissue [110]) where the spacing is also regular. With the model structures described it should be possible to account for such regularity. Chromosome pairing and muscle fibers also contain structures with highly ordered inter-membrane distances.

Numerous other applications of these non-statistical electrostatic methods may be found in the review of membrane structure and function given earlier in this chapter. Among the many interesting problems, too many to delve into detail here, are (1) the peculiar properties of cholesterol in the membrane, (2) the relation of high field values to the radius of curvature in motility studies, (3) mechanisms of trapping of ions in nerve conduction dependent upon geometry of the bilayer and high field values, (4) adhesion properties of macrophages, cancer cells etc. Although the application of these methods to the above and other equally interesting biological problems may be difficult to treat at the molecular level, they will afford rigorous analyses of casual relations from specific molecular structures. The elucidation of structure and function of membraneous systems at the molecular level must also ultimately relate to higher levels of organization.

6 References

1 Rothstein, A., *in*: *Ion exchangers in organic and biochemistry*
ed.: Calmen, C., Kressman, T.R.E. (Interscience, N.Y. 1957).

2 *Specific permselectivity of an anionic membrane relative to chloride and sulfate ions*
DeKorosy, F., Szekely, E., Israel J. Chem. **1** [2a] (1963) 272.

3 *Liquid ion-exchange membranes of extreme selectivity and high permeability for anions*
Sollner, K., Shean, G. M., J. Am. Chem. Soc. **86** (1964) 1901.

4 *Réalisation et étude de membranes lipidique minces présentant une selectivité pour les ions K par rapport aux ions Na*
Dupeyart, M., Menetrier, M.C., Acad. Sc. Paris **258** (1964) 4734.

5 *The frictional coefficients of the flows of non-electrolytes through artificial membranes*
Ginzburg, B. Z., Katchalsky, A., J. Gen. Physiol. **47** [2] (1963) 403.

6 *The electro-osmotic effects arising from the interaction of the selectively anion and selectively cation permeable parts of mosaic membranes*
Carr, C. W., Sollner, K., Biophys. J. **4** [3] (1964) 189.

7 *Electrochemical properties of ionogenic membranes prepared by thermal and oxidative degradation of polyvinyl alcohol*
Ellison, T. M., Spencer, H. G., Polymer Letters No. 1, **1** (1963) 707.

8 *Cellulose acetate membranes: Electron microscopy of structure*
Riley, R., Gardner, J. O., Merten, U., Science **143** [3608] (1964) 801.

9 *Water vapor permeation of selected cellulose ester films*
Patel, M., Patel, J. M., Lemberger, A. P., J. Pharm. Sci. **53** (1964) 286.

10 *Phospholipid membrane model: Importance of phosphatidylserine and its cation exchanger nature*
Nash, A. H., Tobias, J. M., Proc. Natl. Acad. Sci. U.S. **51** (1964) 476.

11 *Diffusion in ion selective membranes*
Caramazza, R., Dorst, W., Hoeve, A. J. C., Staverman, A. J., Trans. Faraday Soc. **59** [490] Part 10 (1963) 2415.

12 *Permselectivity of ion-exchange membranes at high temperatures*
Forgacs, C., Scharf, E., Israel J. Chem. **1** [30] (1963) 267.

13 *Space charge regions in fixed charge membranes and the associated property of capacitance*
Mauro, A., Biophys. J. **2** (1962) 179.

14 *Adsorption from solutions of non-electrolytes*
Kipling, J., J. Chem. Industry (1964) 1007.

15 *Langmuir isotherm in relation to mobility and molecular size of the adsorbate*
Molyneux, P., Nature **202** [4930] (1964) 368.

[16] *The energetics of flocculation and redispersion by polymers*
Healy, T. H., LaMer, V. K., J. Colloid Sci. **19** [4] (1964) 323.

[17] *A study of the description of stearic acid from platinum and surfaces using ellipsometry*
Pimbley, W. T., MacQueen, H. R., J. Phys. Chem. **68** (1964) 1101.

[18] *Polarimetric determination of absorption spectra of thin films on metal*
Churchill, D., Bartell, L. S., J. Phys. Chem. **67** (1963) 2518.

[19] *Surface energy distributions of a homogeneous surface and a heterogeneous surface from argon adsorption isotherms*
Hsieh, P. Y., J. Phys. Chem. **68** (1964) 1068.

[20] *Preparation of a phase diagram for coacervation*
Phares, R. E., Sperandio, G. J., J. Pharm. Sci. **53** (1964) 518.

[21] *The surface area of water preabsorbed on powdered substrates*
Wade, W. H., J. Phys. Chem. **68** (1964) 1029.

[22] *Adsorption of anions at charged sites and phase boundary potentials*
Karreman, G., Bull. Math. Biophys. **26** (1964) 275.

[23] *On the adsorption of ions at charged sites in an electric field II*
Karreman, G., Bull. Math. Biophys. **26** (1964) 139.

[24] *Additivity of intermolecular forces at interfaces I*
Fowkes, F. W., J. Phys. Chem. **67** (1963) 2538.

[25] *Calcium and magnesium binding properties of cell membrane materials*
Carvalho, A. P., Sanui, H., Pace, N., J. Cellular Comp. Physiol. **62** (1963) 311.

[26] *On the physically homogeneous, metal-bound lipid complex of the ox brain*
Hakomori, S., Ishimoda, T., Kowauchi, H., Nakamura, K., J. Biochem. **54** (1963) 458.

[27] *Theory of transport across a membrane model*
Vaidhyanathan, V. S., Perkins, W. H., Towbin, E. J., J. Theor. Biol. **7** (1964) 339.

[28] *Ion transport through cell membrane*
Kimizuka, H., Koketsu, K., J. Theor. Biol. **6** (1964) 290.

[29] *On the permeability of electrolytes through biological membranes*
Vaidhyanathan, V. S., Perkins, W. H., J. Theor. Biol. **7** (1964) 334.

[30] *The concepts of membrane flow and membrane vesiculation as mechanisms for active transport and ion pumping*
Bennett, H. S., J. Biophys. Biochem. Cytol. Suppl. **2** (1956) 99.

[31] *On the permeability of non-electrolytes through biological membranes*
Vaidhyanathan, V. S., Perkins, W. H., J. Theor. Biol. **7** (1964) 334.

[32] *Induced excitability in reconstituted cell membrane structure*
Mueller, P., Rudin, D. O., J. Theor. Biol. **4** (1963) 268.

[33] *Mechanical properties of the red cell membrane II. Visco-elastic breakdown of the membrane*
Rand, R. P., Biophys. J. **4** (1964) 303.

[34] *Low-temperature electron microscopy and X-ray diffraction studies of lipoprotein components in lamellar systems*
Fernandez-Moran, H., Circulation **26** (1962) 1039.

[35] Vreeman, H. J. (private communication) Jan. 16, 1964. Van 't Hof-Laboratorium der Rijksuniversiteit, Utrecht, Sterrenbos 19, Netherlands.

[36] Oneill, C. H., *in: Recent progress in surface science* **1**
ed.: Danielli, J. F., Pankhurst, K. G. A., Riddiford, A. C. (Academic Press, N. Y., 1964) 379.

[37] *The molecular structure of lipid-water systems and cell membrane models studied with the electron microscope*
Stoeckenius, W., Symp. Internatl. Soc. Cell Biol. **1** (Academic Press, N. Y., 1963) 349.

[38 a] *The contractile vacuole and related structures in tetrahymena pyriformis*
Elliot, A. M., Bak, I. J., J. Protozool. **11** [2] (1964) 250.

[38b] *The ultrastructure of cell membranes and their derivatives*
Robertson, J. D., Biochem. Soc. Symp. **16** (1959) 3.

[39] *The electrophoretic behavior of osmium tetroxide-fixed and potassium permanganate-fixed rat erythrocytes*
Glaeser, R. M., Mel, H. C., Biochim. Biophys. Acta **79** (1964) 606.

[40] *Structure and functions of biological membranes*
Kavanau, J. L., Nature **198** [4880] (1963) 525.

[41] *Towards ultra-high magnification*
Mulvey, T., Discovery (June 1964).

[42] *Electron microscopy of the ectoplasm and infra-ciliature of spirostomum ambiguum*
Finley, H., Brown, C., Daniel, W., J. Protozool. **11** (1964) 264.

[43] *Division of labor in the cell*
DeBernard, B., Pan Minerva Medica **9** (1964).

[44] *Studies on the ultrastructure of the nucleoli of the Walker tumor and rat liver*
Smetana, K., Busch, H., Cancer Res. **24** [4] Part 1 (May 1964) 537.

[45] *Cytochrome function in relation to inner membrane structure of mitochondria*
Chance, B., Science **142** (1963) 1176.

[46] *Water permeability of the fetal erythrocyte*
Barton, T. C., Brown, A. J., J. Gen. Physiol. **47** (1964) 839.

[47] *Artificial membranes*
Mueller, P., Rudin, D. O., Tien, H. T., Westcott, W. C., J. Phys. Chem. **67** (1963) 534.

[48] *Black soap films*
Overbeek, J. T. G., J. Phys. Chem. **64** (1960) 1178.

[49] *Artificial membranes*
Huang, C., Wheeldon, L., Thompson, T. E., J. Mol. Biol. **8** [1] (1964) 148.

[50] *The thickness and electrical properties of black hydrocarbon films in aqueous solutions*
Hanaj, T., Haydon, D. A., Taylor, J., Kolloid-Z. **195** [1] (1964) 41.

[51] *Enzyme-bound intermediates in the biosynthesis of mevalonic and palmitic acids*
Brodie, J. D., Wasson, G., Porter, J. W., J. Biol. Chem. **239** (1964) 1346.

[52] *The role of cell-wall lipid in the biosynthesis of bacterial lipopolysaccharide*
Rothfield, L., Horecker, B. L., Proc. Natl. Acad. Sci. U.S. **52** [4] (1964) 939.

[53] *Factors affecting the lysosomal membrane and availability of enzymes*
Sawant, P. L., Dasai, I. D., Tappel, A. L., Arch. Biochem. Biophys. **105** (1964) 247–253.

[54] *Gel filtration of lipid mixtures*
Tipton, C. L., Paulis, J. W., Pierson, M. D., J. Chromatog. **14** (1964) 486.

[55] *The use of sephadex for the removal of non-lipid contaminants from lipid extracts*
Wells, M. A., Dittmer, J. C., Biochem. **2** [6] (1963) 1259.

[56] *Fatty acid composition of lecithin from beef brain and egg yolk*
Kai, M., Joshita, T., Saga, M., J. Biochem. **54** [5] (1963) 403.

[57] *Incorporation of C^{14}-labeled acetate into lipids by macrophages in vitro*
Day, A. J., Fidge, N. H., J. Lipid Res. **5** (1964) 163.

[58] *Etude analytique des lipoprotéines par ultra-centrifugation préparative dans 21 cas d'hyperlipidémies majeures*
Genaes, J. L., Polonovski, J., Ayrault-Jarrier, M., Bard, D., Levy, G., Rev. Franç. Etudes Clin. Biol. **9** [3] (1964) 272.

[59] *Liquid crystalline nature of phospholipids*
Byrne, D., Chapman, D., Nature **202** [4936] (1964) 987.

[60] *Incorporation of fatty acids into phospholipids of erythrocyte membranes*
Oliviera, M. M., Vaughan, M., J. Lipid Res. **5** (1964) 156.

[61] *Separation, identification and quantitative determination of P^{32}-labeled phosphate esters from erythrocytes*
Vanderheiden, B. S., Anal. Biochem. **8** (1964) 1.

[62] *Incorporation of palmitic acid-H^3 into the sphingomelins of the intestinal mucosa of the rat during absorption*
Clement, J., DiCostanzo, G., Biochem. Biophys. Res. Comm. **15** [2] (1964) 163.

[63] *A fluorescent label for the outer components of the plasma membrane*
Maddy, A. H., Biochem. Biophys. Acta **88** (1964) 390.

[64] *Lipids of butanol-treated erythrocytes*
Sloviter, H. A., Tanaka, S., J. Cellular Comp. Physiol. **63** (1964) 261.

[65] *Chemical composition of mycoplasma cells and membranes*
Razin, S., Argaman, M., Avigan, J., J. Gen. Microbiol. **33** (1963) 477.

[66] *The effect of solvent dielectric constant on micellisation by lecithin*
Elworthy, P. H., McIntosh, D. S., Kolloid-Z. **195** (1964) 27.

[67] *Micellization in mixtures of anionic and non-ionic detergents*
Corkill, J. M., Goodman, J. F., Tate, J. R., Trans. Faraday Soc. **60** [497] Part 5 (1964) 986.

[68] *Variations in the micelle size of non-ionic detergents*
Balmbra, R. R., Clunie, J. S., Corkill, J. M., Goodman, J. F., Trans. Faraday Soc. **60** [497] Part 5 (1964) 979.

[69] *Soap films and some problems in surface and colloid chemistry*
Mysels, K. J., J. Phys. Chem. **68** (1964) 341.

[70] *Interactions of mitrochondrial structural protein with phospholipids*
Richardson, S. H., Hultin, H. O., Fleischer, S., Arch. Biochem. Biophys. **105** (1964) 254.

[71] *Molecular sieving by cell membranes of Bacillus megaterium*
Scherrer, R., Gerhardt, P., Nature **204** [4959] (1964) 649.

[72] *Growth of crystals from random close packing*
Bernard, J. D., Knight, K. R., Cherry, I., Nature **202** [4935] (1964) 852.

[73] *Computer search for active site configurations*
Dayhoff, M. O., J. Am. Chem. Soc. **86** (1964) 2295.

[74] Davies, J. T., Rideal, E. K., *Interfacial phenomena* (2nd ed., Academic Press, N. Y., 1963).

[75] *Counter-ion penetration in ionized monolayers at a dielectric interface*
Levine, S., Bell, G. M., Pethica, B. A., J. Chem. Phys. **40** (1964) 2304.

[76] *Changes in the monolayer properties of bovine serum albumin after methylation of its groups*
Korgaonkar, K. S., Desal, A. M., Biochim. Biophys. Acta **79** (1964) 410.

[77] *Properties of ionized monolayers*
Brooks, J. H., Pethica, B. A., Trans. Faraday Soc. **60** [493] Part 1 (1964) 1.

[78] Haydon, D. A., *in: Recent progress in surface science* 1
ed.: Danielli, J. F., Pankhurst, K. G. A., Riddiford, A. C. (Academic Press, N. Y., 1964) 116.

[79] a) *Cell wall potential in nitella*
      b) *Studies on nitella having artificial cell sap., I and II*
      Tazawa, M., Kishimoto, U., Plant Cell Physiol. Tokyo **5** (1964).

[80] *Effect of current on transmembrane potentials in cultured chick heart cells*
      Sperelakis, N., Lehmkuhl, D., J. Gen. Physiol. **47** [5] (1964) 895.

[81] *Transmembrane actions potentials and contractions of human atrial muscle*
      Sleator, W., Gubareff, T., Am. J. Physiol. **206** (1964) 100.

[82] *Effect of detergent on electrical properties of squid axon membrane*
      Kishimoto, U., Adelman, W., J. Gen. Physiol. **47** [5] (1964) 975.

[83] *Depolarization of frogs skeletal muscle membrane by 2,4-dinitrophenol*
      Koketsu, K., Kimizuka, H., Kitamura, R., J. Cellular Comp. Physiol. **63** [2] (1964).

[84] *Electric potentials and Na, K and Cl concentrations in the vacuole and cytoplasm of
      nitella translucens*
      Spanswick, R. M., Williams, F. J., J. Exp. Botany **15** [44] (1964) 193.

[85] *Changes in the membrane permeability of frog's Sartorius muscle fibers in* Ca-*free
      EDTA solution*
      Kimizuka, H., Koketsu, K., J. Gen. Physiol. **47** (1963) 379.

[86] *Streaming potentials in a biological membrane*
      Pidot, A. L., Diamond, J. M., Nature **201** [4920] (1964) 701.

[87] *Cortical intracellular potentials during augmenting and recruiting responses*
      Purpura, D. P., Shofer, R. J., J. Neurophysiol. **27** (1964) 117.

[88] *Membrane properties of barnacle muscle fiber*
      Hagiwara, S., Naka, K., Chichibu, S., Science **143** (1964) 1446.

[89] *A preliminary report on the effects of electric fields on mice*
      Moos, W. S., Aerospace Med. **35** [4] (1964) 374.

[90] *Effects of high frequency electric fields on the living cell-erythrocytes*
      Furedi, A. A., Chad, I., Biochim. Biophys. Acta **79** (1964) 1.

[91] *Swirling of a liquid under the influence of a uniform electric field*
      Brown, D. R., Nature **202** [4935] (1964) 868–870.

[92] *High field effects for linear chains of dipoles on conducting paths of limited length*
      Daniel, V., Vein, P. R., Trans. Faraday Soc. **60** [499] Part 7 (1964) 1310.

[93] *Field controlled ion trapping as a mechanism in nerve membranes*
      Daniel, V., J. Theor. Biol. **6** (1964) 375.

[94] *Dielectric effects of flaws in hydrogen bonding*
      Daniel, V., Trans. Faraday Soc. **60** [499] (1964) 1299.

[95] *Theory of dielectric crystalline dispersion in high polymers*
      Yamafugi, K., Kolloid-Z. **195** [2] (1964) 111.

[96] *The adhesiveness of leukocytes with special reference to zeta potential*
Bongham, A. D., Ann. N.Y. Acad. Sci. **116** Article 3 (August 1964) 945.

[97] *The dynamics of the membrane-bound incompressible body: A mechanism of cellular and subcellular motility*
Weis, P., Proc. Natl. Acad. Sci. U.S. **52** [4] (Oct. 1964) 1024–1029.

[98] *A molecular structural basis for the excitation properties of axons*
Goldman, D. E., Biophys. J. **4** [3] (1964) 167.

[99] *Patterns of assumptions about large molecules*
Pirie, N. W., Arch. Biochem. Biophys. Suppl. **1** (1962) 21.

[100] Hutner, S. H., *in: Introduction* of Biochem. Physiol. Protozoa **3** (1963)1.

[101] Holdane, J. B. S., *in: The planet earth* (*Genesis of life*)
ed.: Bates, D. R. (Pergamon Press, London, 1964).

[102] *The chemical composition and submicroscopic morphology of mycoplasma gallisepticum, Avian PPLO 5969*
Morowitz, H., J. Mol. Biol. **4** (1962) 93.

[103] *The size of small organisms*
Pirie, N. W., Proc. Roy. Soc. London Ser. B **160** (1964) 149.

[104] *Zone melting of organic compounds*
Friedenberg, R., Wilcox, W. R., Back, N., Chem. Rev. **14** (1964) 187.

[105] Stratton, J. A., *Electromagnetic theory* (McGraw-Hill, N.Y., 1941) 160.

[106] *Soap films and some problems in surface and colloid chemistry*
Mysels, K. J., J. Phys. Chem. **68** (1964) 344.

[107] Debye, P., *Polar molecules* (The Chem. Datalog. Co. N.Y., 1929).

[108] Thompson, T. E. (private communication) July 27, 1964, Dept. of Physiological Chemistry, Johns Hopkins University, School of Medicine Baltimore, Maryland 212–5.

[109] Ambrose, E. J., *in: Recent progress in surface science* **1**
ed.: Danielli, J. F., Pankhurst, K. G. A., Riddiford, A. C. (Academic Press, N.Y., 1964) 338.

[110] *Plasma membrane apposition in the central nervous system after aldehyde perfusion*
Karlsson, U., Schultz, R., Nature **201** (1964) 1230.

[111] *The role of water structures in the molecular organisation of cell membranes*
Hechter, O., Neurosci. Res. Program Bull. **2** [5] (1964).

[112] *A macromolecular repeating unit of mitochondrial structure and function*
Fernandez-Moran, H., Oda, T., Blair, P. V., Green, D. E., J. Cell. Biol. **22** (1964) 63.

Preliminary theory and calculations

Part A. Simple methods

Chapter 2

Fixed charge and dipole planar surfaces of finite dimensions

Contents

1 *Introduction*

Representations of biological surfaces and membranes have frequently been analyzed in terms of ionogenic functional organic groupings and polar end groups considered as discrete dipoles and charges [1-3]). Early theoretical physico-chemical analyses of surface films of insoluble substances on liquids at the molecular level [4a]) have interpreted fixed charge distributions in terms of "double layer theory" and surface potential measurements [4b]) and dipole distributions in terms of dipole moments of molecules and contact potentials [4c]). In the latter case, little progress in theory has been made from the Von Helmoltz equation first enunciated in 1873 relating the contact potential of a surface to the dipole moments of its molecules:

$$\Delta V = 4\pi\eta\mu \qquad (1)$$

where ΔV is the change in contact potential, η is the number of molecules of the insoluble film and μ is the vertical component of the dipole moment of one film molecule if all the dipole moments of the film molecules were arranged in a plane. Davies and Rideal in a recent review [5]) have indicated that reorientation of molecules in an ionogenic surface film, resulting from changes in ionic strength in the underlying solution, is of major importance in determination of ΔV. However, in neutral films it has been shown [6]) that surface potential measurements are insensitive to changes in ionic strength. For this reason recent investigations consistently omit dipole effects in analysis of surface phenomena [7]). From a theoretical point of view this has been rationalized by inferences drawn from two simple electrostatic cases. First, an idealized infinite sheet of dipoles of neutral molecules which are aligned perpendicular to the surface has a zero field anywhere normal to the sheet [8]). Secondly, the electric field of a single dipole is proportional to the distance $1/r^3$, thus falling off very rapidly when compared to a single charge whose field is proportional to $1/r^2$. From this position it has been concluded that dipole effects will be negligible compared with charge effects. In the following analysis a non-statistical approach is developed to surface charge distributions and it is shown that dipole effects are significant when compared to fixed charge distributions.

2 Specifications of fixed charge and dipole surface models

Two electrostatic models are considered: (1) a uniform, homogeneous fixed *charge* and (2) a similar *point dipole* distribution upon a circular sheet of radius R (see fig. 9). The distribution is broken up into equal areas such that each charge or dipole is considered to be continuously distributed over an appropriately shaped segment whose area is 25 Å². *
Thus the charge and dipole moment densities may be defined for the two

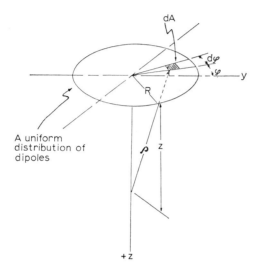

Fig. 9. Flat, circular charge and dipole continuous arrays

sheets as [11]) (1) σ = electronic charge/unit area = 1.6×10^{-19} coulomb/25 Å², (2) p = dipole moment of palmitic acid molecule/unit area = 4.2×10^{-28} coulomb · meter/25 Å².

As it can easily be shown that the x and y components on the axis of symmetry are equal to zero, only the vertical component of the electric field (E_z) is to be described along the axis of symmetry of the sheet. Palmitic acid has been used here, since we thereby obtain a convenient model with a dipole moment of the order of magnitude expected in living membranes.

* This corresponds approximately to the area occupied by a long chain fatty acid molecule in a film derived from force-area curve measurements, at zero pressure.

The assumptions of the model include (1) vacuum conditions, (2) the point dipoles are fixed in the x-y plane but free to rotate, (3) the point dipoles align themselves to a fixed point on the axis of symmetry (z-axis), (4) the field effects of adjacent dipoles on any one dipole are ignored in the alignment process.

3 Derivations

3.1 Fixed charge distribution

Utilizing the inherent symmetry of the model and Coulomb's law (see fig. 9), the electric field on the z-axis for the axis of symmetry of a fixed charge distribution on a circular sheet of radius R is in the positive z-direction and given [9]) by:

$$E_z = + \frac{\sigma}{2\varepsilon_0} \left[1 - \frac{z}{(z^2 + R^2)^{\frac{1}{2}}} \right] \tag{2}$$

where

E_z = electric field intensity
σ = charge/unit area
R = radius of sheet
z = vertical axis of symmetry
ε_0 = permittivity of free space.

3.2 Point dipole distribution

For a similar distribution of fixed point dipoles free to rotate, the electrostatic potential is given by:

$$dU = \frac{1}{4\pi\varepsilon_0} \left[\frac{\boldsymbol{p} \cdot \boldsymbol{\varrho}}{|\varrho|^3} \right] dA \tag{3}$$

where:

U = electrostatic potential
$\boldsymbol{p}$ = dipole moment/unit area
$\boldsymbol{\varrho}$ = a vector from each elemental area to a fixed point on the vertical z-axis.

As

$$E_z = -\nabla U \tag{4}$$

and

$$dE_z = -\nabla \left(\frac{p \cdot \varrho}{4\pi\varepsilon_0 |\varrho|^3} \right) dA \tag{5}$$

then

$$E_z = \int dE_z = -\int_A \int \nabla \left(\frac{p \cdot \varrho}{4\pi\varepsilon_0 |\varrho|^3} \right) dA. \tag{6}$$

Making the following substitutions (cf. fig. 9)

$$p \cdot \varrho = |p||\varrho| \cos \theta \quad \text{where} \quad \theta = 0 \tag{7}$$

$$|\varrho| = (r^2 + z^2)^{\frac{1}{2}}, \tag{8}$$

$$dA = r \, d\varphi \, dr, \tag{9}$$

performing the indicated operations and integrating r from 0 to R, and φ from 0 to 2π yields:

$$E_z = + \frac{|p|}{2\varepsilon_0} \left(\frac{z}{R^2 + z^2} - \frac{1}{z} \right). \tag{10}$$

4 Comparison of the electric field intensity from fixed charge and dipole surfaces

Graphs of eq. (2) and (10) at different values of R are given in figs. 3a, b. To determine the intersection of the two curves for all values of R, eq. (2) and (10) are set equal to each other.

$$E_z(\text{charge}) = E_z(\text{dipole}) \tag{11}$$

if

$$-\frac{\sigma}{2\varepsilon_0} \left(\frac{z}{(z^2 + R^2)^{\frac{1}{2}}} - 1 \right) = -\frac{|p|}{2\varepsilon_0} \left(\frac{z}{R^2 + z^2} - \frac{1}{z} \right). \tag{12}$$

Rearranging yields

$$z^4 - (2p/\sigma)z^3 + R^2 z^2 - (2p/\sigma)R^2 z + R^2 p^2/\sigma^2 = 0 \tag{13}$$

a quartic in z as a function of R. When eq. (13) is solved for R,

$$R = \pm \frac{z}{z - p/\sigma} \sqrt{-z^2 + (2p/\sigma)z} \tag{14}$$

two roots are obtained. From the model, R and z can only have positive values such that

$$R = + \frac{z}{z - p/\sigma} \sqrt{-z^2 + (2p/\sigma)z} \quad \text{where} \quad 2p/\sigma < z \qquad (15)$$

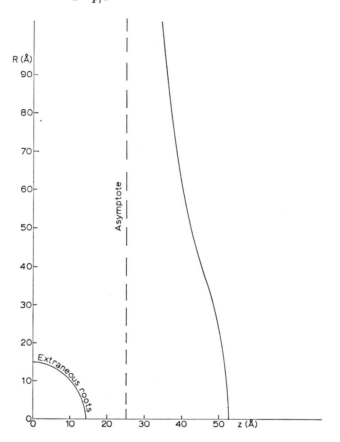

Fig. 10. Graph of eq. (15). Equating charge and dipole fields

and all other roots are extraneous. A graph of eq. (15) (see fig. 10) shows that the electric field intensity of the two sheets will be equivalent, 25–52 Å away from the surface, depending on the radius of the sheet. From fig. 3 it is observed that at distances less than this, the dipole sheet has a larger field than the charged sheet.

5 *Discussion*

The above analysis is intended as a first approximation to determining the maximum electric field beneath a dipole layer, as compared to a fixed charged layer. Intuitively the results described in the previous section appear improbable. Yet rigorous derivations taking into account

(1) dipole–dipole field interactions,
(2) restricted rotation of dipoles,
(3) the distance between dipoles and charges on the sheet assuming a discrete distribution rather than a continuous one,
(4) a distribution of discrete dipoles (a fixed distance between charges making up the dipole),
(5) different positions of the axis of rotation in the discrete dipole case,
(6) the electric field off the axis of symmetry,
(7) the electric field off the axis of symmetry but at points other than the focus of the dipole axes,
(8) other geometrical forms of the sheet,
(9) dielectric constant of an adjacent solution,
(10) the x- and y-components of the electric field,

indicate that the values of the electric field as a function of R and z (see fig. 3) are correct as a first approximation within an order of magnitude.

6 *Summary*

The fact that dipole (polar) end groups in surface films, representative of biological membranes and surfaces, have been neglected in surface chemical calculations is set forth and explained. It is then shown by a non-statistical analysis of the electric field from fixed dipole and charge distributions on an axis of symmetry, that dipole effects can be significant when compared to fixed charges.

7 *References*

[1] Nash, A. H., Tobias, J. M., Proc. Natl. Acad. Sci. U.S. **51** [3] (1964) 476–480.
[2] Carvalho, A. P., Sanui, H., Pace, N., J. Cellular Comp. Physiol. **62** [3] (1963) 311–317.
[3] Stoeckenius, W., Symp. Internatl. Soc. Cell Biol. **1** (Academic Press, N. Y., 1963) 349–367.

[4] (a) Adam, N. K., *The physics and chemistry of surfaces* (3d ed., Oxford University Press, London, 1941) 17–40; (b) ibid., p. 301; (c) ibid., p. 38, p. 135.

[5] Davies, J. T., Rideal, E. K., *Interfacial phenomena* (2nd ed., Academic Press, N. Y., 1963) 70–74.

[6] Frumkin, A. N., Pankratov, K., Acta Phys.-Chim. U.R.S.S. **10** (1939) 45, 55.

[7] Haydon, D. A., *in: Recent progress in surface science* **1**, ed.: Danielli, J. F., Pankhurst, K. G. A., Riddiford, A. C. (Academic Press, N. Y., 1964) 116.

[8] Stratton, J. A., *Electromagnetic theory* (McGraw-Hill, N. Y., 1941) 160.

[9] Reitz, J. R., Milford, F. J., *Foundations of electromagnetic theory* (Addison-Wesley Publ. Co., Reading, Mass., 1962) problem 2.5 p. 42.

[10] Hodgman, C. D. (ed.), *Handbook of chemistry and physics* (39th ed., Chemical Rubber Publ. Co., Cleveland, Ohio, 1957) 295.

[11] McClellan, A. L., *Tables of experimental dipole moments* (W. H. Freeman and Co., San Francisco and London, 1963).

Chapter 3

The potential energy functions
of idealized models of fixed charge
and dipole distributions as related
to surface chemical phenomena

Contents

1 *Introduction*

The problem of calculating the field of a surface containing a set of fixed charges and dipoles has been outlined in chapter 1. It has been shown in chapter 2 as a first approximation that the field on an axis of symmetry of the dipole sheet is as great as the field of a comparable fixed charge distribution, 25–52 Å from the surface depending on the radius R of the sheet. It was also shown that, at closer distances, the electric field of the dipole sheet is greater than that of the charge sheet. Since dipole end groups in surface films and membranes are common and have been consistently neglected in surface field calculations, it is the purpose here to present derivations and a discussion of the potential energy functions, which are also useful in describing these models. The assumptions of the models and the models themselves are those of chapter 2.

The two electrostatic models considered are: (1) a uniform, homogeneous, fixed *charge* and (2) a similar *point dipole* distribution upon a circular sheet of radius R. The charge densities on the two sheets are defined as

$$\sigma = 1.6 \times 10^{-19} \text{ coulombs/25 Å}^2$$

$$|p| = 4.2 \times 10^{-28} \text{ coulomb} \cdot \text{meter/25 Å}^2.$$

The assumptions of the model include (1) vacuum conditions, (2) point dipoles are fixed in the x–y-plane, but free to rotate, (3) the point dipoles align themselves to a fixed point on the axis of symmetry (z-axis), (4) the field effects of adjacent dipoles are neglected.

2 *Derivations*

2.1 *The potential Φ at a point in space on an axis of symmetry under a finite charged sheet*

Using the standard definition of potential [3] *

$$\Phi = -q \int_{\infty}^{z} E_z \cdot dl. \tag{1}$$

Since the field is conservative, it is proper to choose any convenient path, *e.g.*, the axis, over which to integrate. According to chapter 2, eq. (2), the

---

* The potential is defined as the work necessary to move a unit charge from infinity to the point in question.

electric field, E_z, for a point on the z-axis, under the finite charged sheet is given by

$$E_z = \frac{\sigma}{2\varepsilon_0}\left[1 - \frac{z}{(z^2 + R^2)^{\frac{1}{2}}}\right] \tag{2}$$

where

E_z = electric field on axis of symmetry
σ = charge density
z = vertical axis of symmetry
R = radius of the sheet
ε_0 = permittivity of free space.

Arbitrarily choosing

$$d\boldsymbol{l} = dz\hat{k}, \tag{3}$$

such that

$$E_z \cdot d\boldsymbol{l} = E_z dz \tag{4}$$

eq. (2) may be substituted into eq. (1) yielding

$$-\frac{\Phi}{q} = \frac{\sigma}{2\varepsilon_0}\lim_{a\to\infty}\left(\int_a^z dz - \int_a^z \frac{z\,dz}{\sqrt{z^2 + R^2}}\right). \tag{5}$$

Performing the indicated integrations

$$-\frac{\Phi}{q} = \frac{\sigma}{2\varepsilon_0}(z - \sqrt{z^2 + R^2}) + \frac{\sigma}{2\varepsilon_0}\lim_{a\to\infty}(-a + \sqrt{a^2 + R^2}). \tag{6}$$

The term

$$-a + \sqrt{a^2 + R^2} = -a + a\sqrt{1 + R^2/a^2} \tag{7}$$

may be expanded by the binomial theorem as follows

$$\left(1 + \frac{R^2}{a^2}\right)^{\frac{1}{2}} = 1 + \frac{1}{2}\frac{R^2}{a^2} - \frac{1}{4}\left(\frac{R^2}{a^3}\right)^2 + \ldots \tag{8}$$

Substituting eq. (8) into eq. (7) and finally into eq. (6) yields upon rearranging

$$-\frac{\Phi}{q} = \frac{\sigma}{2\varepsilon_0}(z - \sqrt{z^2 + R^2}) + \frac{\sigma}{2\varepsilon_0}\lim_{a\to\infty}\left(\frac{1}{2}\frac{R^2}{a^2} - \frac{1}{4}\frac{R^4}{a^3} + \ldots\right). \tag{9}$$

Taking the limit, all terms of the series approach zero as a increases towards infinity. Therefore,

$$\Phi = \frac{\sigma q}{2\varepsilon_0}(\sqrt{z^2 + R^2} - z). \qquad (10)$$

It may be easily shown from eq. (10) that as $z \to \infty$ the potential tends to 0.

2.2 *The potential Φ at a point in space on an axis of symmetry under a finite dipole sheet*

In a similar manner (as indicated in chapter 2) the electric field has been given for a point on the z-axis under a finite dipole sheet as

$$E_z = \frac{|p|}{2\varepsilon_0}\left[\frac{1}{z} - \frac{z}{z^2 + R^2}\right]. \qquad (11)$$

(The domain under the sheet is considered negative here.) Substituting eq. (11) into eq. (1) using the conditions of eq. (3) and (4) yields

$$\Phi = -\frac{q|p|}{2\varepsilon_0}\lim_{a \to \infty}\int_a^z \frac{dz}{z} - \int_a^z \frac{z\,dz}{z^2 + R^2}. \qquad (12)$$

Performing the necessary integrations we obtain

$$\Phi = -\frac{q|p|}{2\varepsilon_0}\lim_{a \to \infty}\left[\ln z - \ln a - \tfrac{1}{2}\ln(z^2 + R^2) + \tfrac{1}{2}\ln(a^2 + R^2)\right]. \qquad (13)$$

Rearranging yields

$$\Phi = \frac{q|p|}{2\varepsilon_0}\left[\ln\frac{\sqrt{z^2 + R^2}}{z} + \lim_{a \to \infty}\frac{a}{\sqrt{a^2 + R^2}}\right]. \qquad (14)$$

In order to evaluate the limit it is noted that

$$\frac{a}{\sqrt{a^2 + R^2}} = \frac{1}{\sqrt{1 + R^2/a^2}}. \qquad (15)$$

Therefore

$$\Phi = \frac{q|p|}{2\varepsilon_0}\ln\frac{\sqrt{z^2 + R^2}}{z}. \qquad (16)$$

It may easily be shown that in eq. (16) as $z \to \infty$, $\Phi \to 0$.

3 *Discussion*

In fig. 6 eq. (10) and (16) are plotted for various values of R. For comparison, the potential energy of a single point dipole and a single point charge are plotted in the same figure as well as the value of kT at 300 °K. It may be observed that although the potential energy of the charge sheet is an order of magnitude or so larger than the dipole sheet both sheets yield energies four to five orders of magnitude larger than kT. Thus the presence of a dielectric in the adjoining medium (to be described in detail in chapter 12), will at most reduce the energies by one to two orders of magnitude. These facts point to the possibility of long range interactions (at distances > 100 Å) between surfaces (corresponding to these model systems) and macromolecules in solution. The use of additional parameters (as will also be described in chapters 7–12) will reduce the energies at most by an order of magnitude still yielding remarkably high values. Such factors as dipole–dipole interactions on the sheet, discrete dipoles rather than point dipoles, summation technique taking into account finite distances between dipoles rather than a continuous distribution, and the energies off the axis of symmetry, have been analyzed and do not essentially alter the picture.

At present, surface potential measurement techniques have been inadequate to make measurements at points sufficiently close to a surface to provide an experimental check on the calculations made here. Yet field intensity and potential measurements are technologically well within reach of this achievement [4, 5]. The fact that the potential energy *does* vary with distance from a dipole sheet with remarkably high values greater than 100 Å away may explain numerous ordering processes that occur with DNA, and macromolecular replication in general. The experimental verification of this type of long range interaction will be a significant step in the biological field.

4 *Summary*

The potential energy functions are derived for simple electrostatic models of fixed charge and dipole distributions on a surface of finite dimensions. These functions when compared with the similar functions for a single point charge, a single point dipole, and a value of kT indicate that long range (distances > 100 Å) interactions may occur between surfaces and macromolecules in solution.

Chapter 4

The influence of geometry on idealized models of fixed charge and dipole distributions

Contents

1 *Introduction*

Field and potential singularities for unbounded, idealized fixed charge distributions have been characterized for some time in electrostatic theory [1]). Little has been done in showing the correspondence between these highly idealized models and their counterpart in real physical-chemical surfaces. In chapters 2 and 3, simple models and equations have been developed for bounded, homogeneous fixed charge and dipole distributions on a circular sheet. The purpose here is to show the relationships between the field singularities of electrostatic theory and the equations for fixed charge and dipole models previously presented. Additional geometrical distributions of fixed charges and dipoles are also to be analyzed and discussed here.

It is to be noted, as has been pointed out in the literature [1]), that field and potential singularities do not actually exist in nature (i.e. unbounded sheets do not exist). However, these singularities are useful, in as much as the fields and potentials that do occur around bounded simple geometrical configurations, are often indistinguishable over the space concerned. It is also to be noted that if either surface or line fixed charge distributions are infinite in dimensions, the potential cannot be referred to infinity. Thus, it is necessary to speak of potential singularities as the behavior of the potential *near* the distribution.

It will also be the purpose of this chapter to extend the concept of singularities from idealizations of real *charges* as points, lines and surfaces, to real *dipoles*, represented as idealizations of point dipoles, rods and surface distributions. This permits great mathematical simplicity and offers convenient concepts for describing and representing actual fields.

A complicating factor in the analysis that follows is that the volume integrals extending over the source charges and dipoles for a bounded distribution, are commonly thought not to lead to singular values of the fields or potentials. However, with the additional distributions to be described in this chapter, whose equations are seemingly similar, it is more likely that the above singularities form the basis of these equations with given geometric factors determining their form. Thus, a combination of geometric factors and singularities should ultimately determine the mathematical form of all bounded distributions. An analysis in this chapter using this approach shows how one specific geometric factor may be superimposed upon a set of singular functions to yield a set of equations for bounded distributions. Similar analyses have long been known in classifying field functions of differential equations [2]).

Results from studies on van der Waals' attractive forces common in the literature will also be included. The purpose here is to point out another form of field and potential singularities which have not previously been classified as such. However, no original work has been added in analyzing these geometrical forms other than that which is already current in the literature.

2 *Field singularities*

Table 1 classifies three sets of field singularities taken from the literature and analyses to be given here. The unbounded fixed charge distributions are well characterized [1]). The fixed dipole distributions are based upon an analysis of the fields generated assuming a free alignment of all the

TABLE 1

Field singularities

Type of distribution	Fixed charge	Fixed dipole	Oscillating dipole	Fixed charge	Fixed dipole	Oscillating dipole
Point	z^{-2}	z^{-3}	z^{-8}	z^{-1}	z^{-2}	z^{-7}
Line or rod	z^{-1}	z^{-2}		$\ln z$	z^{-1}	
Surface	constant	z^{-1}	z^{-4}	z	$\ln z$	z^{-3}

dipoles (in the distribution) to a given point beneath the array. The rationale for allowing the dipoles to swing freely in a surface distribution is given in chapter 8. Suffice it to say here that realignment of dipoles in surface chemical studies has been neglected and dipole field effects considered negligible. An extension of the dipole model to multipoles in general, assuming a realignment to the field point, and a rigid array of multipoles in the distribution which are free to rotate, is given in table 2. The correspondence of such higher multipole model systems to real physical chemical systems will be considered in chapter 8. The derivations for the equations and singularities given in table 2 are similar to the

TABLE 2

Field singularities of point charges and multipoles for infinite sheets assuming complete alignment to the field point

n	Field equation	Singular value	$K = $ Charge density constants
1	$E_z = K'$	constant	$\sigma = \dfrac{\text{point charge}}{\text{unit area}}$
2	$E_z = K'' z^{-1}$	z^{-1}	$|\boldsymbol{p}| = \dfrac{\text{dipole moment}}{\text{unit area}}$
3	$E_z = K''' z^{-2}$	z^{-2}	$|\boldsymbol{\lambda}| = \dfrac{\text{quadrupole moment}}{\text{unit area}}$
4	$E_z = K'''' z^{-3}$	z^{-3}	$|\boldsymbol{\chi}| = \dfrac{\text{octapole moment}}{\text{unit area}}$

$E_z = K z^{1-n}$ $(n = 1, 2, 3, 4 \ldots)$.

analyses for infinite sheets given in the appendix of this chapter. These equations may be generalized into a single field equation given at the bottom of table 2. The appendix gives the derivations for an infinite sheet and an infinite rod of dipoles aligned to a point beneath the distribution. The oscillating dipole singularities arise from the analysis of the van der Waals'–London dispersion forces between two neutral atoms or a surface of neutral atoms and a point beneath it [3]).

It is of some interest to compare these singularities with the bounded circular distributions for fixed charges and dipoles on an axis of symmetry (ch. 2, eqs. (2) and (10))

$$E_z(\text{charge}) = -\frac{\sigma}{2\varepsilon_0}\left(\frac{z}{(z^2+R^2)^{\frac{1}{2}}} - 1\right) \tag{1}$$

$$E_z(\text{dipole}) = -\frac{|\boldsymbol{p}|}{2\varepsilon_0}\left(\frac{z}{R^2+z^2} - \frac{1}{z}\right). \tag{2}$$

From equations (1) and (2) it is observed that if $z \le R$ (where $R = $ radius of sheet) the field intensity is very close to that of the infinite sheet as given in table 1. Thus, it may be shown in the general case that as a first approximation, the field close to a finite or bounded sheet, is similar to the infinite case.

3 *Equations of bounded distributions*

Table 3 lists the field and potential energy functions for finite fixed charge and dipole distributions of varied geometry. The equations for the field and potential for the fixed charge distributions may be derived simply from Coulomb's law. The derivations for the equations of the dipole distributions are similar to those for the infinite cases given in the appendix, section 6.1, with the additional geometric conditions imposed.

The application of the previously described singularities to finite bounded arrays may be most easily understood by analyzing, as an example, the axial symmetric case of a flat, circular distribution. One may consider the field generated by the finite sheet as composed of two parts: (1) the singularity and (2) the geometric factor. In the axial symmetric circular case, the geometric factor may be considered as:

$$\left[1 - \left(\frac{z}{(z^2 + R^2)^{\frac{1}{2}}}\right)^n\right] \tag{3}$$

where $n = 1, 2, 3 \ldots$. The singularity for an infinite plane is given by:

$$E_z = Kz^{1-n} \qquad \text{(from table 2)}. \tag{4}$$

Combining these two factors yields:

$$E_z = [Kz^{1-n}]\left[1 - \left(\frac{z}{(z^2 + R^2)^{\frac{1}{2}}}\right)^n\right] \tag{5}$$

for finite circular sheets. Eq. (5) may then be used to generate the following set of equations which have been verified independently of this method:

$n = 1$, for a circular sheet of fixed point charges

$$E_z = K'\left[1 - \frac{z}{(z^2 + R^2)^{\frac{1}{2}}}\right]; \tag{6}$$

$n = 2$, for a circular sheet of fixed point dipoles

$$E_z = K''z^{-1}\left[1 - \frac{z^2}{z^2 + R^2}\right]; \tag{7}$$

$n = 3$, for a circular sheet of fixed point quadrupoles

$$E_z = K'''z^{-2}\left[1 - \frac{z^3}{(z^2 + R^2)^{\frac{3}{2}}}\right]. \tag{8}$$

TABLE 3

The influence of geometry on idealized models of fixed charge and dipole distributions
R is half the length of a side or rod, ϱ is the radius

Type of charge distribution	Fixed charge		Fixed dipole	
	E_z	Φ	E_z	Φ
Finite rod	$\dfrac{\lambda R}{2\pi\varepsilon_0}\left[\dfrac{1}{z(z^2+R^2)^{\frac{1}{2}}}\right]$	$\dfrac{\lambda q}{4\pi\varepsilon_0}\ln\left[\dfrac{(z^2+R^2)^{\frac{1}{2}}+R}{z}\right]$	$\dfrac{|p|}{2\varepsilon_0}\left[\dfrac{R}{z(z^2+R^2)}+\dfrac{1}{z}\tan^{-1}\dfrac{R}{z}\right]$	$\dfrac{q|p|}{2\pi\varepsilon_0}\left[\dfrac{1}{z}-\tan^{-1}\dfrac{R}{z}\right]$
Semi-circular rod	$\dfrac{\lambda}{4\pi\varepsilon_0|\varrho|}$		$\dfrac{|p|}{\pi\varepsilon_0|\varrho|^2}$	
Hemispherical sheet	$\dfrac{\sigma}{4\varepsilon_0}$		$\dfrac{|p|}{2\varepsilon_0|\varrho|}$	
Finite circular sheet	$\dfrac{\sigma}{2\varepsilon_0}\left[\dfrac{z}{(z^2+R^2)^{\frac{1}{2}}}-1\right]$	$\dfrac{\sigma q}{2\varepsilon_0}\left[\sqrt{z^2+R^2}-z\right]$	$-\dfrac{|p|}{2\varepsilon_0}\left[\dfrac{z}{z^2+R^2}-\dfrac{1}{z}\right]$	$\dfrac{q|p|}{2\varepsilon_0}\ln\sqrt{\dfrac{z^2+R^2}{z}}$
Finite square sheet	$\dfrac{\sigma}{\pi\varepsilon_0}\tan^{-1}\left[\dfrac{R^2}{z\sqrt{2R^2+z^2}}\right]$		$\dfrac{2|p|}{\pi\varepsilon_0}\left[\dfrac{\tan^{-1}(R/2z)}{\frac{1}{2}R}\right.$ $-\dfrac{z}{(R/z)\sqrt{z^2+(R/z)^2}}\tan^{-1}\dfrac{\frac{1}{2}R}{\sqrt{z^2+(R/z)^2}}$ $\left.+\dfrac{\frac{1}{2}R}{z\sqrt{z^2+(R/z)^2}}\tan^{-1}\dfrac{\frac{1}{2}R}{\sqrt{z^2+(R/z)^2}}\right]$	

There are three kinds of relationships pertaining to bounded distributions to be distinguished from tables 1–3. The first most obvious relation is proceeding from a point, to one dimension (a line), to two dimensions (a surface). Thus, singularities are useful in characterizing the fields generated from one level of organization of matter to another.

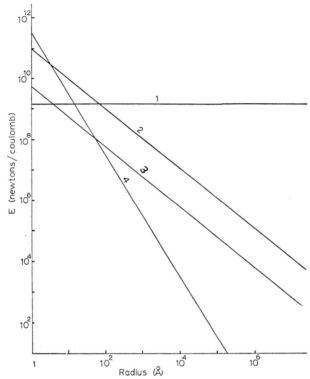

Fig. 11. Electric field intensity at the geometrical center of the distributions as a function of the radius

Curve 1, hemispherical charged sheet   Curve 3, semicircular charged rod
Curve 2, hemispherical dipole sheet   Curve 4, semicircular dipole rod

The second relation involves the *kind* of distribution. Although only three kinds of distributions (fixed charge, fixed dipole, oscillating dipole) have been rigorously considered corresponding to real systems, quadrupoles, octapoles and, in the general case, multipoles may also be analysed.

The third relation involves a geometrical factor allowing one to proceed from one bounded form to another by means of the singularities already analyzed. Sufficient data are not yet available on enough geometrical distributions to allow generalizations at this time. However, table 3 does indicate various similarities in the form of the equations of similar geometries.

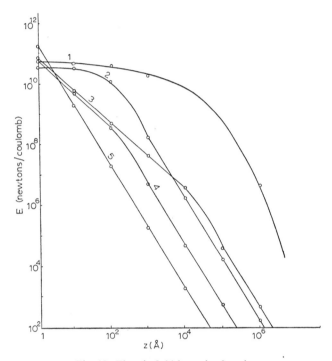

Fig. 12. Electric field intensity functions

Curve 1, finite charged plate, $R=10^{-6}$ m   Curve 3, finite charged rod, $R=10^{-6}$ m
Curve 2, finite charged plate, $R=10^{-8}$ m   Curve 4, finite charged rod, $R=10^{-8}$m
Curve 5, point charge

4 Discussion

In previous chapters, it has been pointed out that the correspondence of a fixed electrostatic charge and dipole distribution model has its counterpart in ionogenic and polar monomolecular surface films. It has also been shown that biological surfaces and membranes are rarely ionized with a full compliment of charge upon them. Rather, most biological surfaces are composed of molecules with polar groups represented as dipoles. Thus, the equations of tables 1–3 confirm the previously determined fact that the hitherto neglected fixed dipole effects may be as

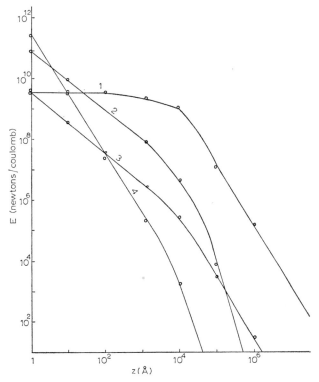

Fig. 13. Electric field intensity functions ($R = 10^{-6}$ m)
Curve 1, finite charged sheet   Curve 3, finite charged rod
Curve 2, finite dipole sheet   Curve 4, finite dipole rod

significant as fixed charge effects. Thus, comparisons of one- and two-dimensional bounded arrays of fixed charges and dipoles (see figs. 11–15) yield significantly similar field and potential values. In a similar manner, the influence of geometry on the distribution alters little the order of magnitude of the field effects. Close to a distribution, the infinite arrays

of both charges and dipoles (field singularities) offer a convenient means
of generalizing the order of magnitude of the field and potential independent of the geometry of the bounded distributions (see fig. 6).

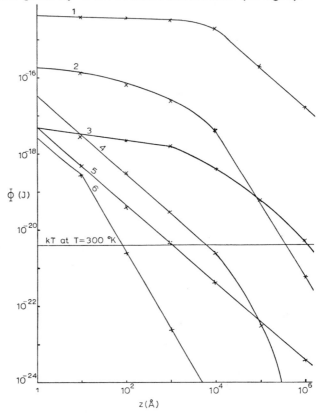

Fig. 14. Potential energy functions

Curve 1, finite charged sheet, $R=10^{-6}$ m   Curve 2, finite dipole sheet, $R=10^{-6}$ m
Curve 3, finite charged rod, $R=10^{-6}$ m   Curve 4, finite dipole rod, $R=10^{-6}$ m
Curve 5, point charge   Curve 6, point dipole

5 Summary

An analysis of field singularities from distributions of fixed charges, fixed
dipoles and oscillating dipoles indicates their usefulness in approximating
the field and potential of bounded arrays of diverse geometries for the
spatial extent close to the distribution. A comparison of the field and

potential effects from bounded arrays of fixed charge and dipole distributions as given in table 3 confirms the previously described fact that fixed dipole effects yield as significantly high values as fixed charges when close to the array.

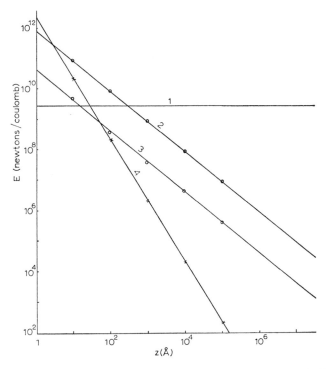

Fig. 15. Electric field intensity as a function of distance from the distribution
Curve 1, infinite charged sheet   Curve 3, infinite charged rod
Curve 2, infinite dipole sheet   Curve 4, infinite dipole rod

6 Appendix

6.1 Derivation of the electric field intensity due to a uniform dipole distribution along an infinite rod

Assume an electric dipole moment (point dipole) per unit length of p. In addition, assume complete freedom of rotation of the dipoles noting that p and ϱ (cf. fig. 16) are collinear so that the dot product $\boldsymbol{p} \cdot \boldsymbol{\varrho}$ reduces to $p\varrho$.

$$E = -\nabla U. \tag{1}$$

From fig. 16

$$dE = -\nabla \left[\frac{\boldsymbol{p} \cdot \boldsymbol{\varrho}}{4\pi\varepsilon_0 |\varrho|^3} \, dy \right]. \tag{2}$$

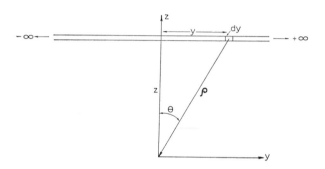

Fig. 16. Electric field for an infinite dipole rod

But

$$dE = (dE)_x \hat{\imath} + (dE)_y \hat{\jmath} + (dE)_z \hat{k}. \tag{3}$$

Then

$$dE = -\frac{\partial}{\partial y} \frac{|\boldsymbol{p}| dy}{4\pi\varepsilon_0 \, \varrho^2} \hat{\jmath} - \frac{\partial}{\partial z} \frac{|\boldsymbol{p}| dy}{4\pi\varepsilon_0 \, \varrho^2} \hat{k}. \tag{4}$$

However, the x and y components of the electric field intensity are zero, due to the symmetry of geometrical configuration. Therefore,

$$dE = dE_z = -\frac{\partial}{\partial z} \frac{|\boldsymbol{p}| dy}{4\pi\varepsilon_0 \, \varrho^2} \tag{5}$$

$$E_z = \int_{-\infty}^{+\infty} (dE_z). \tag{6}$$

Letting

$$\varrho^2 = y^2 + z^2 \tag{7}$$

$$y = z \tan\theta \qquad dy = z \sec^2\theta \, d\theta, \tag{8}$$

making the necessary substitutions into eqs. (5) and (6) and changing
the limits of integration yields

$$E_z = \frac{|\boldsymbol{p}|z}{2\pi\varepsilon_0} \int_{-\pi/2}^{+\pi/2} \frac{z\sec^2\theta\,d\theta}{z^4(1+\tan^2\theta)^2}. \tag{9}$$

Utilizing the symmetry involved and performing the integration yields

$$E_z = \frac{|\boldsymbol{p}|}{4\varepsilon_0 z^2}. \tag{10}$$

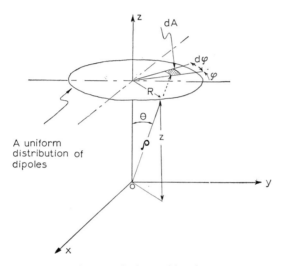

Fig. 17. Dipole considerations

6.2 *Derivation of the electric field intensity due to a uniform dipole distribution on an infinite sheet*

Using the same assumptions of derivation 1 in this appendix and noting
that eq. (1) holds then from fig. 17

$$d\boldsymbol{E} = -\nabla \frac{\boldsymbol{p}\cdot\boldsymbol{\varrho}}{4\pi\varepsilon_0|\boldsymbol{\varrho}|^3}\,dA \tag{11}$$

and

$$dE_z = -\frac{\partial}{\partial\varrho}\frac{p\,dA}{4\pi\varepsilon_0\varrho^2}\,\hat{\varrho} \tag{12}$$

since all x, y terms cancel out due to symmetry. Using the identities

$$dA = \varrho \sin \theta \, d\varphi \, dr = \varrho z \sin \theta \, d\varphi \, d\theta + \varrho \sin^2 \theta \, d\varphi \, d\varrho$$

and performing the indicated operations in eq. (12) yields

$$dE_z = \frac{|\mathbf{p}| \cos \theta}{2\pi\varepsilon_0 \, \varrho^3} (\varrho z \sin \theta \, d\theta \, d\varphi + \varrho \sin^2 \theta \, d\varrho \, d\varphi). \tag{13}$$

Since

$$E_z = \int_A \int dE_z \tag{14}$$

rearranging eq. (13) and substituting into eq. (14) gives

$$E_z = \frac{|\mathbf{p}|z}{2\pi\varepsilon_0} \int_0^{2\pi} \int_0^{\pi/2} \frac{\sin \theta}{\varrho^3} \, d\theta \, d\varphi + \frac{|\mathbf{p}|z}{2\pi\varepsilon_0} \int_0^{2\pi} \int_0^{\infty} \frac{\sin^2 \theta}{\varrho^3} \, d\varrho \, d\varphi. \tag{15}$$

Letting $z = \varrho \cos \theta$ from fig. 17 and performing the integrations yields

$$E_z = \frac{|\mathbf{p}|}{4z\varepsilon_0} + \frac{|\mathbf{p}|z}{2\varepsilon_0 \, z^2} - \frac{|\mathbf{p}|z^3}{4\varepsilon_0 \, z^4}. \tag{16}$$

Rearranging yields

$$E_z = \frac{|\mathbf{p}|}{2\varepsilon_0 \, z}. \tag{17}$$

7 Equations for figures 3–8

Electric field on the axis of symmetry of a flat circular sheet

Charge sheet:

$$E_z = -\frac{\sigma}{2\varepsilon_0} \left(\frac{z}{(z^2 + R^2)^{\frac{1}{2}}} - 1 \right)$$

Dipole aligned sheet:

$$E_z = -\frac{|\mathbf{p}|}{2\varepsilon_0} \left(\frac{z}{z^2 + R^2} - \frac{1}{z} \right)$$

Dipoles perpendicular to sheet:

$$E_z = -\frac{|\mathbf{p}|}{2\varepsilon_0} \left(\frac{1}{(z^2 + R^2)^{\frac{1}{2}}} \right) \left(\frac{z^2}{z^2 + R^2} - 1 \right)$$

Dipoles lying flat in the plane:

$$E_z = -\frac{|p|}{2\varepsilon_0}\frac{1}{z}\frac{R^3}{(z^2+R^2)^{\frac{3}{2}}}$$

Potential energy on the axis of symmetry of a flat circular sheet
Charge sheet:

$$\Phi = \frac{\sigma q}{2\varepsilon_0}\left[(z^2+R^2)^{\frac{1}{2}}-z\right]$$

Dipole aligned sheet:

$$\Phi = \frac{|p|q}{2\varepsilon_0}\frac{\ln (z^2+R^2)^{\frac{1}{2}}}{z}$$

Dipoles perpendicular to sheet:

$$\Phi = \frac{|p|q}{2\varepsilon_0}\left(1-\frac{z}{(z^2+R^2)^{\frac{1}{2}}}\right)$$

Dipoles lying flat in the plane:

$$\Phi = \frac{|p|q}{2\varepsilon_0}\left[\ln\left(\frac{(R^2+z^2)^{\frac{1}{2}}-R}{z}\right)+\frac{R}{(R^2+z^2)^{\frac{1}{2}}}\right]$$

where:

$z =$ distance from sheet along axis of symmetry
$R =$ radius of the sheet
$\sigma =$ charge density $= q/25$ Å^2
$|p| =$ dipole moment density $= p/25$ Å^2
$q = 1.6\times 10^{-19}$ coulombs (charge of an electron)
$p = 4.2\times 10^{-28}$ coulomb · meters
$\varepsilon_0 =$ permittivity of free space.

8 *References*

[1] Panofsky, W. K. H., Phillips, M., *Classical electricity and magnetism* (Addison–Wesley Publ. Co., Reading, Mass., 1956) 11–13.
[2] Moon, P., Spencer, D. E., *Field theory handbook* (Springer-Verlag, Berlin, 1961).
[3] Overbeek, J. Th. G., J. Phys. Chem. **64** (1960) 1178.

Preliminary theory and calculations

Part B. Refinements

Chapter 5

Electric field calculations of charge and dipole model membrane systems

Contents

1 *Introduction*

In chapters 2–4 simplified analyses of a model of fixed charge and dipole distributions have been presented. Assuming alignment of dipoles to a field point on a vertical axis of symmetry beneath the distribution, the electric field and potential values at the field point were found to be significant when compared to a fixed charge sheet.

The purpose of this chapter is twofold:

(1) to determine the electric field *off* the axis of symmetry at any point beneath a fixed distribution of *dipoles* focussed at the point.

(2) to determine the electric field *off* the axis of symmetry at any point beneath a fixed distribution of *charges*.

The calculated field values are graphed for comparison purposes.

With the advent of computer methods using numerical techniques, it is possible to arrive at a simple evaluation of the field at a position off the axis of symmetry for large distributions of fixed charges and dipoles relevant to the study of biological membranes. The *assumptions* involved for the model systems in order to be applicable to the biological case, and the methods underlying the computations may be summarized as follows:

1. The two electrostatic models considered are:
   (a) a uniform, homogeneous, fixed *charge* and
   (b) a similar *point dipole* distribution upon a square sheet, whose length of side R equals 177 Å. (The length of side was chosen such that the area of the square would equal the area of the circular distributions discussed in ch. 2 with a radius R equal to 100 Å.)

2. The charge densities on the two sheets are defined as:
   (a) $\sigma = 1.6 \times 10^{-19}$ coulombs/25 Å^2
   (b) $|p| = 4.2 \times 10^{-28}$ coulomb $\cdot$ meters/25 Å^2

3. It is assumed that these models represent one half of the biological membrane neglecting water molecules, electrolyte and the influence of the other half of the membrane.

4. The point dipoles are fixed in the x–y plane but are free to rotate.

5. The point dipoles align themselves to any point beneath the array where the field is being calculated.

6. The field effects of adjacent dipoles on the sheet are neglected.

7. The derivation of equations used to evaluate the fields for the two

models is given in sections 4.1 and 4.2. The accuracy of the calculation employed is dependent upon the procedure for rounding off digits stored in the computer. Errors arise for only small values of E ($E < 100$) which are rare. As an example, all values on the axis of symmetry calculated in closed form in ch. 2 are identical to all corresponding computer values.

The above assumptions have been outlined in chapter 1 and may be justified by considering the maximum first order effects adjacent to the sheets. Dipole interactions and field values on the sheet will be considered in chapters 6 and 7.

2 *Discussion*

The graphical analysis given in figs. 18–32 utilizes the symmetry of the field values over the entirety of the square sheet. Thus the graphs represent one quadrant (or one fourth) of the square since the field is symmetric with respect to the x and y planes. (With one exception, fig. 32 shows an edge view of the whole sheet.) Holding two of the coordinates constant one of the three field vectors (E_x, E_y or E_z) is plotted against the third

TABLE 1

Electric field intensity component plotted for a coordinate of the field point for a dipole and charge square sheet

Fig.			
26	x vs. E_x	$y = 90$ Å	$z = 100$ Å
27	x vs. E_x	$y = 250$ Å	$z = 100$ Å
28	x vs. E_x	$y = 90$ Å	$z = 200$ Å
29	x vs. E_x	$y = 250$ Å	$z = 200$ Å
22	z vs. E_z	$x = 90$ Å	$y = 90$ Å
23	z vs. E_z	$x = 250$ Å	$y = 90$ Å
20	z vs. E_z	$x = 250$ Å	$y = 250$ Å
21	x vs. E_z	$y = 90$ Å	$z = 100$ Å
18	x vs. E_z	$y = 250$ Å	$z = 100$ Å
19	x vs. E_z	$y = 90$ Å	$z = 200$ Å
24	x vs. E_z	$y = 250$ Å	$z = 200$ Å
25	z vs. E_x	$x = 90$ Å	$y = 90$ Å
30	z vs. E_x	$x = 90$ Å	$y = 250$ Å
31	z vs. E_x	$x = 250$ Å	$y = 250$ Å

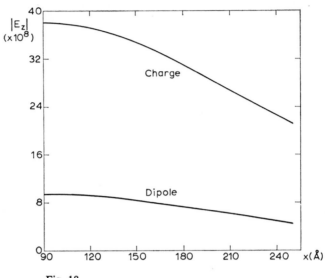

Fig. 18

Fig. 19

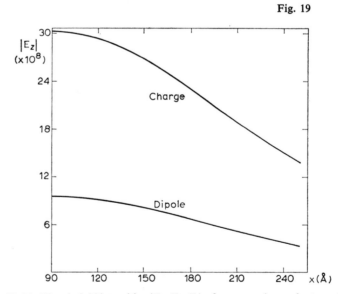

Figs. 18–31. Electric field intensities (E_x, E_y, E_z) of a square charge sheet as a function of distance (variables for each separate figure are given in table 1 and the horizontal axes correspond to the heavy lines of fig. 32b; $R = 177$ Å throughout)

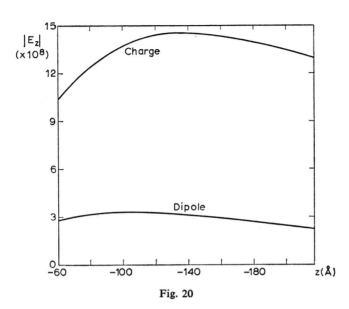

Fig. 20

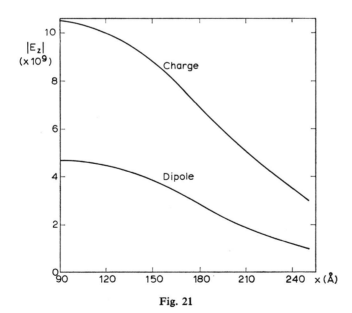

Fig. 21

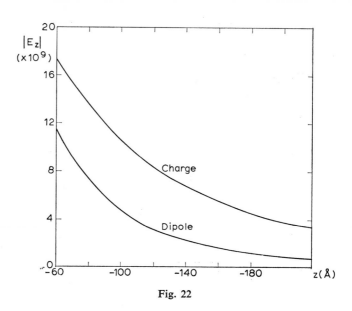

Fig. 22

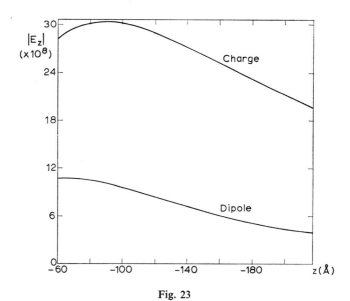

Fig. 23

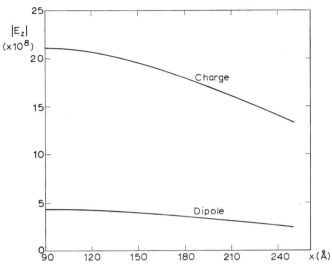

Fig. 24

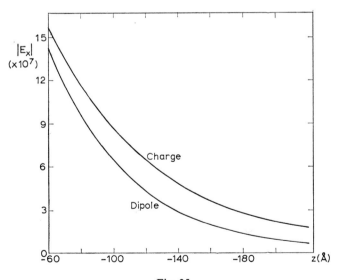

Fig. 25

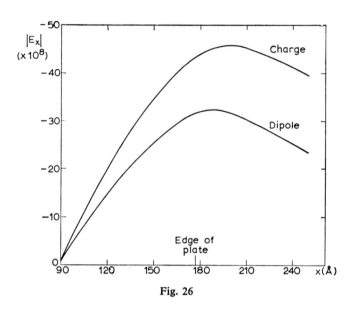

Fig. 26

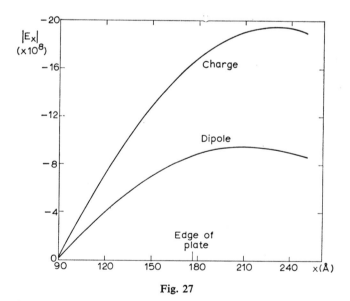

Fig. 27

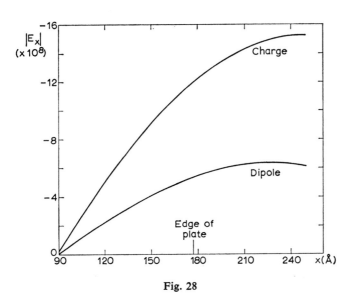

Fig. 28

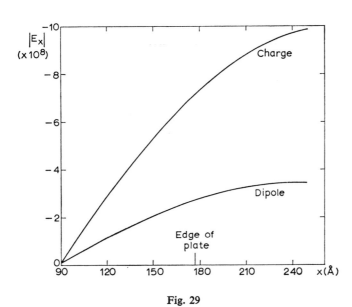

Fig. 29

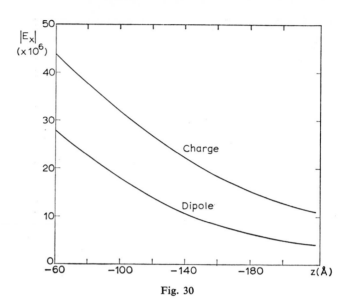

Fig. 30

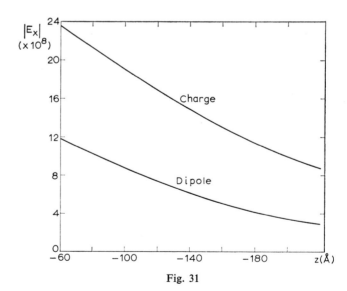

Fig. 31

coordinate. The analysis is further simplified by the fact that E_x is symmetric to E_y so that only one of these vectors is graphed. Table 1 and fig. 32b show the coordinates chosen for analysis.

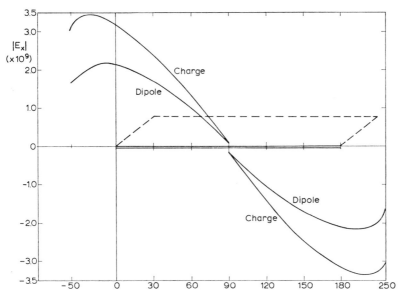

Fig. 32a. E_x field component of square charge and dipole sheet as a function of distance (edge view; $z = 100$, $y = 180$, $s = 177$ Å)

In general, for most field points, the charged sheet has a field slightly larger than that from the dipole sheet. This finding is similar to that of the axial symmetric analyses described in chapters 2–4. Considering only the E_z component of the total field, the previous, on the axis derivations, showed a functional decrease in field as the distance from the sheet increased. This fact is confirmed for the axis of symmetry of the square sheet in fig. 22. However, for points off the axis of symmetry, the field E_z tends to be small close to the sheet, rising to a maximum and then decreasing at substantial distances. These parabolic curves are shown in figs. 20 and 23. This finding is quite significant for biological systems as it indicates that in certain nonaxial cases, the field increases to a maximum as a function of distance before falling off in the usual manner. In a similar way, the E_x and E_y components are equal to zero on the axis of symmetry, increase to a maximum at some point under the sheet (depending on the x, y and z coordinates) and then decrease at some distance

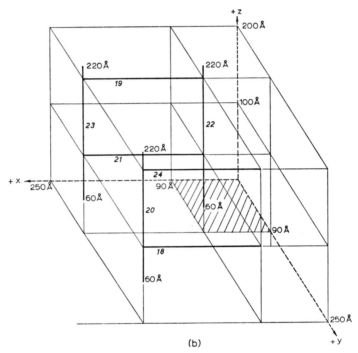

(b)

Fig. 32b. Heavy lines are sets of x, y, z-values for which E_z is calculated and plotted in figs. 18–24. Slanting numbers refer to these figures. Hatched: one quadrant of the sheet. The figure represents one octant of the space around the sheet

past the edge of the sheet. These parabolic curves given in figs. 26–29, 32a indicate the wide variations in field effects of E_x and E_y components in the off-axial cases.

To further illustrate the wide variation in field effects of a square charged sheet contour maps representing equipotential or isopotential surfaces * are given in figs. 33–40. Representative planes were chosen to show the changes in E_x and E_z components as a function of distance.

* Maps representing contours of equal field intensity.

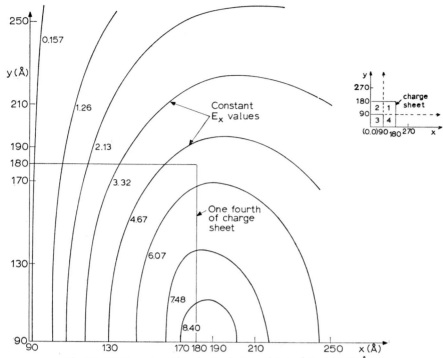

Fig. 33. $10^9 E_x$ contour lines in the first quadrant of the $z = 60$ Å plane

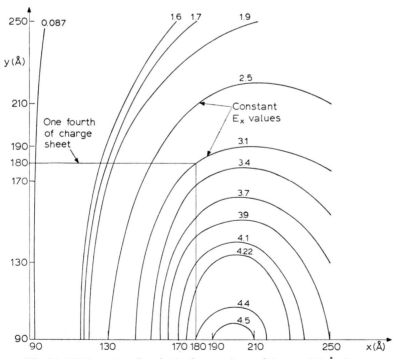

Fig. 34. $10^9 E_x$ contour lines in the first quadrant of the $z = 100$ Å plane

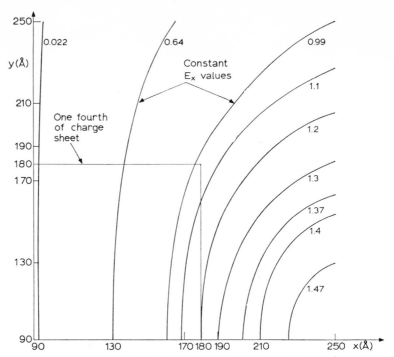

Fig. 35. $10^9 E_x$ contour lines in the first quadrant of the $z = 200$ Å plane

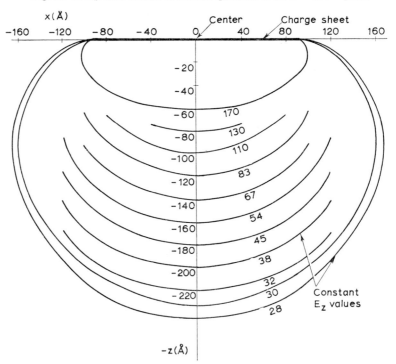

Fig. 36. $10^8 E_z$ contour lines in the $y = 0$ Å plane

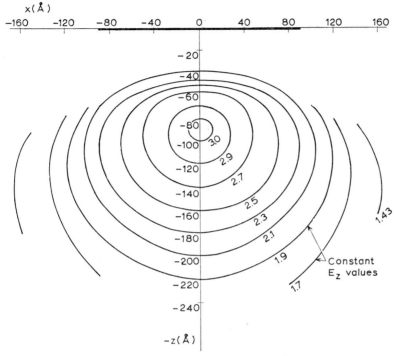

Fig. 37. $10^9 E_z$ contour lines in the $y = 250$ Å plane

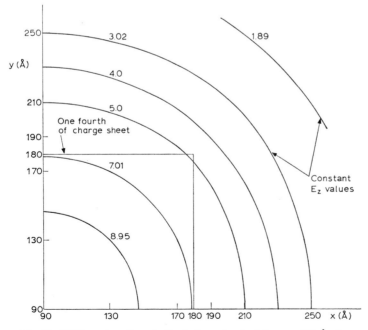

Fig. 38. $10^9 E_z$ contour lines in the first quadrant of the $z = 100$ Å plane

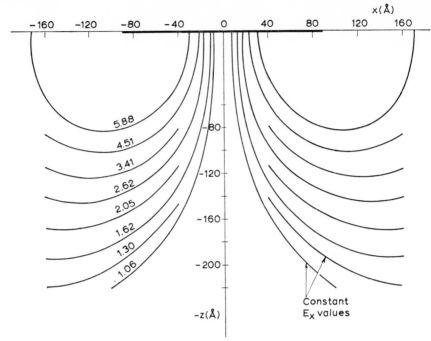

Fig. 39. $10^9 E_x$ contour lines in the $y = 90$ Å plane

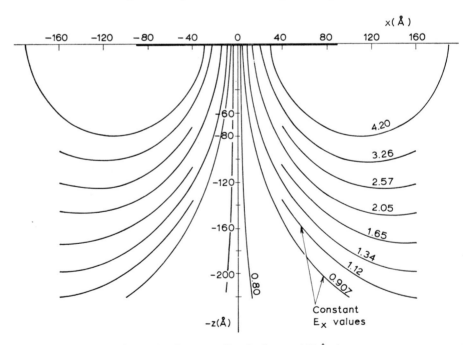

Fig. 40. $10^9 E_x$ contour lines in the $y = 180$ Å plane

3 *Summary*

Calculations are made for the components of the field for electrostatic models of a fixed charge and dipole square sheet. The contributions to the field in non-axial positions indicate that the components of the field *increase* as a function of distance until they reach a *maximum* where they then *decrease* in the normal manner. In the axial position, the field decreases as a function of position confirming analyses described in previous chapters of comparisons of axial symmetric charge and dipole fields.

4 *Appendix*

4.1 *Derivation of dipole model*

It is the purpose of this derivation to determine components of the electrostatic field intensity at an arbitrary field point *x, y, z*, underneath a homogeneous point dipole distribution. See (5) below. It is assumed that all the dipoles align to whatever field point is chosen and that the dipoles are distributed upon a square of dimensions $s \times s$ (see fig. 41).

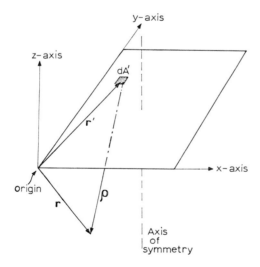

Fig. 41. Analysis of electric field for a square dipole distribution

Nomenclature

1. Define: $r' = x'\hat{\imath} + y'\hat{\jmath}$ (1)
   which locates the source point

2. Define: $r = x\hat{\imath} + y\hat{\jmath} + z\hat{k}$ (2)
   which locates the field point. If $x = s/2$, $y = s/2$, the field point is located on the axis of symmetry.

3. Define: $\varrho = r - r' = (x - x')\hat{\imath} + (y - y')\hat{\jmath} + z\hat{k}$ (3)
   as a vector from the source point to the field point.

4. Let primed symbols represent source variables.

5. Define: p = dipole moment/unit area and assume $|p|$ to be constant.

For the dipole distributions discussed in ch. 2–4

$$dE = -\nabla \left[\frac{p \cdot \varrho}{4\pi\varepsilon_0 |\varrho|^3} \, dA' \right] \tag{4}$$

where p and ϱ are collinear but of opposite sense such that

$$p \cdot \varrho = -|p||\varrho| \tag{5}$$

Thus

$$dE = +\nabla \left[\frac{p}{4\pi\varepsilon_0 |\varrho|^2} \, dA' \right]. \tag{6}$$

But from eq. (3)

$$|\varrho|^2 = (x - x')^2 + (y - y')^2 + z^2 \tag{7}$$

$$dE = dE_x \hat{\imath} + dE_y \hat{\jmath} + dE_z \hat{k} \tag{8}$$

then, substituting eq. (7) in eq. (6) and performing the indicated operations, yields

$$dE_x = -\frac{|p|(x - x')dA'}{2\pi\varepsilon_0[(x - x')^2 + (y - y')^2 + z^2]^2}, \tag{9}$$

$$dE_y = -\frac{|p|(y - y')dA'}{2\pi\varepsilon_0[(x - x')^2 + (y - y')^2 + z^2]^2}, \tag{10}$$

$$dE_z = -\frac{|p|z\,dA'}{2\pi\varepsilon_0[(x - x')^2 + (y - y')^2 + z^2]^2}. \tag{11}$$

It is now necessary to integrate eqs. (9), (10) and (11) over the entire distribution to obtain the field components at a point (x, y, z). Noting that

$$dA' = dx' dy' \tag{12}$$

and the limits of integration are

$$x' = 0 \rightarrow x' = s$$
$$y' = 0 \rightarrow y' = s \tag{13}$$

one obtains

$$E_x = -\frac{|p|}{2\pi\varepsilon_0} \int_{y'=0}^{s} \int_{x'=0}^{s} \frac{(x-x')dx'dy'}{[(x-x')^2 + (y-y')^2 + z^2]^2}, \tag{14}$$

$$E_y = -\frac{|p|}{2\pi\varepsilon_0} \int_{y'=0}^{s} \int_{x'=0}^{s} \frac{(y-y')dx'dy'}{[(x-x')^2 + (y-y')^2 + z^2]^2}, \tag{15}$$

$$E_z = -\frac{|p|}{2\pi\varepsilon_0} \int_{y'=0}^{s} \int_{x'=0}^{s} \frac{dx'dy'}{[(x-x')^2 + (y-y')^2 + z^2]^2}. \tag{16}$$

The evaluation of these integrals yields the following set of equations:

$$
\begin{aligned}
E_z(x, y, z) = \frac{|p|}{4\pi\varepsilon_0} \Bigg[&-\frac{y}{z(y^2+z^2)^{\frac{1}{2}}} \tan^{-1}\left[\frac{x}{(y^2+z^2)^{\frac{1}{2}}}\right] \\
&+\frac{y}{z(y^2+z^2)^{\frac{1}{2}}} \tan^{-1}\left[\frac{x-s}{(y^2+z^2)^{\frac{1}{2}}}\right] \\
&-\frac{y-s}{z[(y-s)^2+z^2]^{\frac{1}{2}}} \tan^{-1}\left[\frac{x-s}{[(y-s)^2+z^2]^{\frac{1}{2}}}\right] \\
&+\frac{y-s}{z[(y-s)^2+z^2]^{\frac{1}{2}}} \tan^{-1}\left[\frac{x}{[(y-s)^2+z^2]^{\frac{1}{2}}}\right] \\
&-\frac{x-s}{z[(x-s)^2+z^2]^{\frac{1}{2}}} \tan^{-1}\left[\frac{y-s}{[(x-s)^2+z^2]^{\frac{1}{2}}}\right] \\
&+\frac{x}{z(x^2+z^2)^{\frac{1}{2}}} \tan^{-1}\left[\frac{y-s}{(x^2+z^2)^{\frac{1}{2}}}\right] \\
&+\frac{x-s}{z[(x-s)^2+z^2]^{\frac{1}{2}}} \tan^{-1}\left[\frac{y}{[(x-s)^2+z^2]^{\frac{1}{2}}}\right] \\
&-\frac{x}{z(x^2+z^2)^{\frac{1}{2}}} \tan^{-1}\left[\frac{y}{(x^2+z^2)^{\frac{1}{2}}}\right] \Bigg],
\end{aligned} \tag{17}
$$

$$E_x(x, y, z) = \frac{|p|}{2\pi\varepsilon_0}\left[\frac{1}{[(x-s)^2+z^2]^{\frac{1}{2}}}\tan^{-1}\left[\frac{y-s}{[(x-s)^2+z^2]^{\frac{1}{2}}}\right]\right.$$

$$-\frac{1}{(x^2+z^2)^{\frac{1}{2}}}\tan^{-1}\left[\frac{y-s}{(x^2+z^2)^{\frac{1}{2}}}\right]$$

$$-\frac{1}{[(x-s)^2+z^2]^{\frac{1}{2}}}\tan^{-1}\left[\frac{y}{[(x-s)^2+z^2]^{\frac{1}{2}}}\right]$$

$$\left.+\frac{1}{(x^2+z^2)^{\frac{1}{2}}}\tan^{-1}\left[\frac{y}{(x^2+z^2)^{\frac{1}{2}}}\right]\right], \tag{18}$$

$$E_y(x, y, z) = \frac{|p|}{2\pi\varepsilon_0}\left[\frac{1}{[(y-s)^2+z^2]^{\frac{1}{2}}}\tan^{-1}\left[\frac{x-s}{[(y-s)^2+z^2]^{\frac{1}{2}}}\right]\right.$$

$$+\frac{1}{(y^2+z^2)^{\frac{1}{2}}}\tan^{-1}\left[\frac{x}{(y^2+z^2)^{\frac{1}{2}}}\right]$$

$$-\frac{1}{[(y-s)^2+z^2]^{\frac{1}{2}}}\tan^{-1}\left[\frac{x}{[(y-s)^2+z^2]^{\frac{1}{2}}}\right]$$

$$\left.-\frac{1}{(y^2+z^2)^{\frac{1}{2}}}\tan^{-1}\left[\frac{x-s}{(y^2+z^2)^{\frac{1}{2}}}\right]\right]. \tag{19}$$

Equations (17), (18) and (19) satisfy the conditions

(a) $\lim\limits_{x,\,y\to\frac{1}{2}s} E_x(x, y, z) \to 0$

(b) $\lim\limits_{x,\,y\to\frac{1}{2}s} E_y(x, y, z) \to 0$

(c) $\lim\limits_{z\to\infty} E_z(x, y, z) \to 0$

(d) $\lim\limits_{z\to\infty} E_x(x, y, z) \to 0$

(e) $\lim\limits_{z\to\infty} E_y(x, y, z) \to 0$

and the total field at a point (x, y, z) under the distribution is given by

$$E_{total}(x, y, z) = E_x(x, y, z)+E_y(x, y, z)+E_z(x, y, z) \tag{20}$$

where eqs. (17), (18) and (19) may be substituted into eq. (20).

4.2 *Derivation of charge model*

The purpose of this derivation is to determine the integrals necessary to evaluate the field E at any point beneath a finite, square, fixed charged sheet.

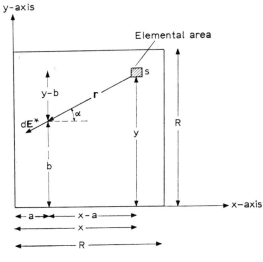

Fig. 42a

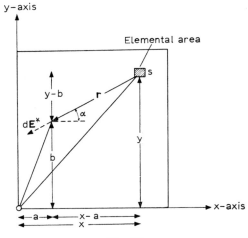

Fig. 42b

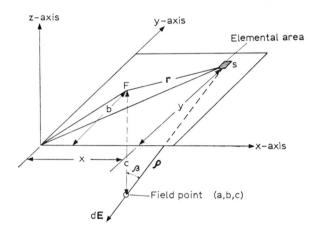

Fig. 42c

Figs. 42a, b, c. Analysis of electric field for a square charge distribution

Definitions (from fig. 42)

1. Let coordinates x, y locate source points
2. Let coordinates a, b, c locate field points
3. Let $\sigma = $ a surface charge density (coulomb/meter^2)

Therefore

$$dq = dA. \qquad (1)$$

4. Let $r^2 = (x-a)^2+(y-b)^2$ (Pythagorean theorem)

$$\varrho^2 = c^2+r^2$$
$$\varrho^2 = c^2+(x-a)^2+(y-b)^2. \qquad (2)$$

From the definition of the field

$$dE = \frac{dq\,\hat{\varrho}}{4\pi\varepsilon_0\,\varrho^2}. \qquad (3)$$

Substituting eqs. (1) and (2) into (3) yields

$$dE = \frac{\sigma\,dA}{4\pi\varepsilon_0[c^2+(x-a)^2+(y-b)^2]}\,\hat{\varrho}. \qquad (4)$$

At any general field point there will be three components of the field

$$E_{total} = E_x(a, b, c) + E_y(a, b, c) + E_z(a, b, c). \tag{5}$$

First determining E_z,

$$dE_z = dE \cos \beta. \tag{6}$$

But

$$\cos \beta = \frac{c}{[c^2 + (x-a)^2 + (y-b)^2]^{\frac{1}{2}}}. \tag{7}$$

Therefore substituting eqs. (6) and (7) into (4) yields

$$dE_z = \frac{\sigma c \, dx \, dy}{4\pi\varepsilon_0 [c^2 + (x-a)^2 + (y-b)^2]^{\frac{3}{2}}}. \tag{8}$$

Integrating over the entire distribution gives

$$E_z(a, b, c) = \int_{x=x_1}^{x=x_2} \int_{y=y_1}^{y=y_2} \frac{\sigma c \, dx \, dy}{4\pi\varepsilon_0 [c^2 + (x-a)^2 + (y-b)^2]^{\frac{3}{2}}}. \tag{9}$$

To determine the x and y components it is necessary to project dE onto the x, y plane. Let dE^* be this projection. Then

$$dE^* = dE \sin \beta. \tag{10}$$

But from fig. 42

$$\sin \beta = \frac{r}{\varrho} = \frac{[(x-a)^2 + (y-b)^2]^{\frac{1}{2}}}{[c^2 + (x-a)^2 + (y-b)^2]^{\frac{1}{2}}}. \tag{11}$$

Therefore

$$dE^* = \frac{\sigma \, dA}{4\pi\varepsilon_0 [c^2 + (x-a)^2 + (y-b)^2]^{\frac{1}{2}}} \frac{[(x-a)^2 + (y-b)^2]^{\frac{1}{2}}}{[c^2 + (x-a)^2 + (y-b)^2]^{\frac{1}{2}}}. \tag{12}$$

Since the projection of dE^* on the x-axis is dE_x and on the y-axis dE_y, then

$$dE_x = dE^* \cos \alpha \tag{13}$$

where

$$\cos \alpha = \frac{x-a}{r} = \frac{x-a}{[(x-a)^2 + (y-b)^2]^{\frac{1}{2}}}. \tag{14}$$

Substituting eqs. (12) and (14) into (13) and rearranging yields

$$dE_x = \frac{\sigma(x-a)dx\,dy}{4\pi\varepsilon_0[c^2+(x-a)^2+(y-b)^2]^{\frac{3}{2}}}.$$ (15)

Integrating eq. (15) yields the total x-component of E at the field point (a, b, c)

$$E_x(a, b, c) = \int_{x=x_1}^{x=x_2}\int_{y=y_1}^{y=y_2} \frac{\sigma(x-a)dx\,dy}{4\pi\varepsilon_0[c^2+(x-a)^2+(y-b)]^{\frac{3}{2}}}.$$ (16)

To obtain the y-component of E, it is noted that

$$dE_y = dE^* \sin\alpha$$ (17)

where

$$\sin\alpha = \frac{y-b}{r} = \frac{y-b}{[(x-a)^2+(y-b)^2]^{\frac{1}{2}}}.$$ (18)

Substituting eqs. (18) and (12) into (17), and rearranging yields

$$dE_y = \frac{\sigma(y-b)dx\,dy}{4\pi\varepsilon_0[c^2+(x-a)^2+(y-b)^2]^{\frac{3}{2}}}.$$ (19)

Integrating eq. (19) yields the total y-component of E at the point (a, b, c)

$$E_y(a, b, c) = \int_{x=x_1}^{x=x_2}\int_{y=y_1}^{y=y_2} \frac{\sigma(y-b)dx\,dy}{4\pi\varepsilon_0[c^2+(x-a)^2+(y-b)^2]^{\frac{3}{2}}}.$$ (20)

If the square sheet is required to have the same area as a circular sheet of $R = 10^{-8}$ m (for purposes of comparison), then one side of the square s is given by

$$s^2 = \pi R^2$$ (21)

$$s = 1.77248 \times 10^{-8} \text{ m.}$$ (22)

Therefore the limits on the integration become

$$x = 0 \rightarrow x = 1.77248 \times 10^{-8} \text{ m}$$
$$y = 0 \rightarrow y = 1.77248 \times 10^{-8} \text{ m.}$$ (23)

The integrals of equations (9), (16) and (20), using the limits of integration given in (23), along with the total field given in equation (5) have been programmed on an IBM 1620 using Simpson's rule. Increments of $h = 100$ units, and $h = 20$ units were utilized. The % error calculated in using $h = 20$ was 0.0003 %. The plots of values obtained are given in figs. 18–32.

Chapter 6

Electric field intensity theory as applied to model systems of idealized fixed dipoles and point charges

Contents

1 *Introduction*

In chapters 1–5 a model has been developed for the field and potential functions for fixed dipole and charge distributions. The development of this model system has proceeded from specific first approximations by simple electrostatic treatments of on the axis of symmetry derivations, to the more general cases of calculating the field anywhere beneath these sheets. This chapter is concerned with refinements of these treatments with reference to *modifications* of the model.

The subject may be divided into four parts. The first consists of derivations and computer analysis of a distribution of eight dipoles which are considered from three points of view.

The three representations utilized take into account

1. The point dipole discrete approach as distinguished from continuous distributions as in chapters 2–4.
2. Discrete dipoles, taking into account a charge separation and free rotation about a fixed positive end.
3. Discrete dipoles, taking into account a charge separation and free rotation about a fixed center of the charge separation.

The *point dipole* continuous approach (chs. 1–5) has been utilized in previous derivations and is considered the most general and simplest kind of representation. The *fixed positive end of the discrete case* corresponds to a lecithin molecule where there is free rotation of the polar group. Modifications of this model would yield the fatty acid molecule which has *restricted* rotation about the polar group. The *discrete center of rotation* case corresponds to a molecule of cholesterol or cholesterone where the entire molecule acts as a rigid rotator (rigid dumbell). The computer analysis of these cases compares field values in the plane of the distribution. Thus field values which are obtained on the sheet should be a first approximation for the biological double, dipole layered membrane, where experimental verification already exists [1]).

The second part of the chapter consists of the derivation of equations for determining the electric field intensity on an axis of symmetry of a uniform dipole distribution (1681 dipoles), where the dipoles are considered as discrete units with a charge separation. The equations for the field normal to the sheet are first derived using a summation procedure and then evaluated on an IBM 1620 computer.

The third aspect involves the calculation of error incurred by assuming a homogeneous, fixed charge distribution rather than an actual discrete, fixed charged case. This involves a computer analysis of the comparison of the integration procedure with a summation procedure for fixed charges.

The fourth problem to be taken up involves finding the percent difference between the discrete and point dipole treatment of a large finite distribution. This is established by considering the computer analysis of field points in the plane of a distribution of 400 dipoles on a plate 100 Å^2.

2 Derivations

A. The object of these first analyses is to examine three different modifications for dipole distributions as regards their field effects in the plane of the distribution. In all three cases the same distribution was employed (i.e. eight dipoles distributed 5 Å apart in the positive-x, positive-y quadrant of the plane). The three conditions for dipoles analyzed are:

Case 1. Charge separated dipole free to rotate about its midpoint. (About the center of the dumbell – cholesterol molecule.)

Case 2. Idealized point dipole.

Case 3. Charge separated dipole free to rotate about its positive tip. (About the top of the dumbell – lecithin molecule.)

In all cases, the origin is chosen as the field point (see figs. 43–45). Throughout the analyses it is assumed that the dipoles are free to align in an external field. (A positive charge at $z = -100$ Å.) Furthermore, dipole–dipole interactions are neglected. The value used for the charge separation distance is $l = 3 \text{ Å} = 3 \times 10^{-10}$ m. The value for the dipole moment is $p = 4.2 \times 10^{-28}$ coulomb · meter. Thus $|p| = q|l|$ and

$$q = \frac{|p|}{|l|} = 1.4 \times 10^{-18} \text{ coulomb.} \tag{1}$$

Case 1 (see fig. 43)

Definitions:

1. Let

$$r_i = x_i i + y_i j \tag{2}$$

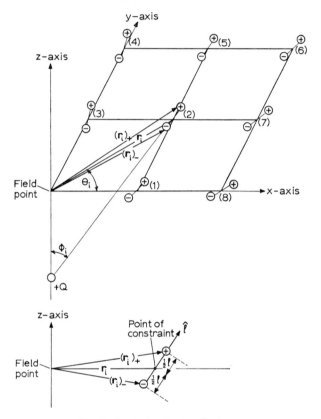

Fig. 43. Analysis of point dipole array

locate the midpoint of the ith dipole. All midpoints are located in the x-y plane.

2.   Define l_i as a unit vector along the axis of the ith dipole from the negative charge to the positive charge.

3.   Let

$$(r_i)_+ = r_i + \tfrac{1}{2} l l_i \tag{3}$$

locate the positive charge of the ith dipole.

4.   Let

$$(r_i)_- = r_i - \tfrac{1}{2} l l_i \tag{4}$$

locate the negative charge of the ith dipole.

5.   Define θ_i as the angle between r_i and the positive x-axis.

6.   Define φ_i as the angle between the z-axis and the axis of the ith dipole.

The analysis is divided into two parts. First, the field at (0) due to the positive charges is determined, and second, the field due to the negative charges at (0) is found. If $(E_i)_+$ denotes the field at (0) due to the ith positive charge, then

$$(E_i)_+ = \frac{q(r_i)_+}{4\pi\varepsilon_0(r_i)_+^3}.$$ (5)

But from the defining equations (2) and (3)

$$(r_i)_+ = x_i\mathbf{i} + y_i\mathbf{j} + \tfrac{1}{2}l\mathbf{l}_i.$$ (6)

And from fig. 43

$$l_i = \sin\varphi_i\cos\theta_i\mathbf{i} + \sin\varphi_i\sin\theta_i\mathbf{j} + \cos\varphi_i\mathbf{k}$$ (7)

noting that

$$\sin\varphi_i = \frac{r_i}{(z^2 + r_i^2)^{\frac{1}{2}}}$$ (8)

$$\cos\varphi_i = \frac{z}{(z^2 + r_i^2)^{\frac{1}{2}}}$$ (9)

$$\sin\theta_i = y_i/r_i$$ (10)

$$\cos\theta_i = x_i/r_i.$$ (11)

Substituting eqs. (8–11) into (7) yields

$$l_i = \frac{x_i}{(r_i^2 + z^2)^{\frac{1}{2}}}\mathbf{i} + \frac{y_i}{(r_i^2 + z^2)^{\frac{1}{2}}}\mathbf{j} + \frac{z}{(r_i^2 + z^2)^{\frac{1}{2}}}\mathbf{k}.$$ (12)

Thus combining eqs. (6) and (12), and rearranging yields

$$(r_i)_+ = x_i\left[1 + \frac{\tfrac{1}{2}l}{(x_i^2 + y_i^2 + z^2)^{\frac{1}{2}}}\right]\mathbf{i}$$

$$+ y_i\left[1 + \frac{\tfrac{1}{2}l}{(x_i^2 + y_i^2 + z^2)^{\frac{1}{2}}}\right]\mathbf{j}$$

$$+ \left[\frac{\tfrac{1}{2}zl}{(x_i^2 + y_i^2 + z^2)^{\frac{1}{2}}}\right]\mathbf{k}.$$ (13)

But by definition

$$(\mathbf{r}_i)_+ = x_i \mathbf{i} + y_i \mathbf{j} + z\mathbf{k} \tag{14}$$

and

$$|(\mathbf{r}_i)_+| = [(x_i)^2 + (y_i)^2 + (z)^2]^{\frac{1}{2}}. \tag{15}$$

Therefore, after making the necessary substitutions of eqs. (14) and (15) into (13) and collecting terms, gives

$$|(\mathbf{r}_i)_+| = \left[x_i^2 + y_i^2 + \frac{l(x_i^2 + y_i^2)}{(x_i^2 + y_i^2 + z^2)^{\frac{1}{2}}} + \frac{l^2}{4} \right]^{\frac{1}{2}} \tag{16}$$

and

$$|(\mathbf{r}_i)^3_+| = \left[x_i^2 + y_i^2 + \frac{l(x_i^2 + y_i^2)}{(x_i^2 + y_i^2 + z^2)^{\frac{1}{2}}} + \frac{l^2}{4} \right]^{\frac{3}{2}}. \tag{17}$$

It is now possible to substitute into eq. (5) for the terms $(\mathbf{r}_i)^3_+$ and $(\mathbf{r}_i)_+$. Breaking this equation into components and summing over i from $1 \to 8$, the field components can be determined at (0) due to the positive charges:

$$(E_x)_+ = \sum_{i=1}^{8} (E_{ix})_+ \tag{18}$$

$$(E_y)_+ = \sum_{i=1}^{8} (E_{iy})_+ \tag{19}$$

$$(E_z)_+ = \sum_{i=1}^{8} (E_{iz})_+ . \tag{20}$$

Thus

$$(E_x)_+ = -\frac{q}{4\pi\varepsilon_0} \sum_{i=1}^{8} \frac{x_i \left(1 + \dfrac{\frac{1}{2}l}{(x_i^2 + y_i^2 + z^2)^{\frac{1}{2}}} \right)}{\left[x_i^2 + y_i^2 + \dfrac{l(x_i^2 + y_i^2)}{(x_i^2 + y_i^2 + z^2)^{\frac{1}{2}}} + \dfrac{l^2}{4} \right]^{\frac{3}{2}}} \tag{21}$$

$$(E_y)_+ = -\frac{q}{4\pi\varepsilon_0} \sum_{i=1}^{8} \frac{y_i \left(1 + \dfrac{\frac{1}{2}l}{(x_i^2 + y_i^2 + z^2)^{\frac{1}{2}}} \right)}{\left[x_i^2 + y_i^2 + \dfrac{l(x_i^2 + y_i^2)}{(x_i^2 + y_i^2 + z^2)^{\frac{1}{2}}} + \dfrac{l^2}{4} \right]^{\frac{3}{2}}} \tag{22}$$

$$(E_z)_+ = -\frac{q}{4\pi\varepsilon_0}\sum_{i=1}^{8}\frac{\frac{1}{2}zl}{(x_i^2+y_i^2+z^2)^{\frac{1}{2}}}{\left[x_i^2+y_i^2+\frac{l(x_i^2+y_i^2)}{(x_i^2+y_i^2+z^2)^{\frac{1}{2}}}+\frac{l^2}{4}\right]^{\frac{3}{2}}}.\tag{23}$$

In a similar manner, the field at **0** due to the *i*th negative charge is given by:

$$(E_x)_- = \frac{q}{4\pi\varepsilon_0}\sum_{i=1}^{8}\frac{x_i\left(1-\frac{\frac{1}{2}l}{(x_i^2+y_i^2+z^2)^{\frac{1}{2}}}\right)}{\left[x_i^2+y_i^2-\frac{l(x_i^2+y_i^2)}{(x_i^2+y_i^2+z^2)^{\frac{1}{2}}}+\frac{l^2}{4}\right]^{\frac{3}{2}}}\tag{24}$$

$$(E_y)_- = \frac{q}{4\pi\varepsilon_0}\sum_{i=1}^{8}\frac{y_i\left(1-\frac{\frac{1}{2}l}{(x_i^2+y_i^2+z^2)^{\frac{1}{2}}}\right)}{\left[x_i^2+y_i^2-\frac{l(x_i^2+y_i^2)}{(x_i^2+y_i^2+z^2)^{\frac{1}{2}}}+\frac{l^2}{4}\right]^{\frac{3}{2}}}\tag{25}$$

$$(E_z)_- = -\frac{q}{4\pi\varepsilon_0}\sum_{i=1}^{8}\frac{\frac{1}{2}zl}{(x_i^2+y_i^2+z^2)^{\frac{1}{2}}}{\left[x_i^2+y_i^2-\frac{l(x_i^2+y_i^2)}{(x_i^2+y_i^2+z^2)^{\frac{1}{2}}}+\frac{l^2}{4}\right]^{\frac{3}{2}}}.\tag{26}$$

The field at **0** is then equal to

$$E = E_+ + E_-\tag{27}$$

or in component form

$$E_x = (E_x)_+ + (E_x)_-\tag{28}$$

$$E_y = (E_y)_+ + (E_y)_-\tag{29}$$

$$E_z = (E_z)_+ + (E_z)_-.\tag{30}$$

CASE 2 (see fig. 44)

Definitions:

1. Let the *i*th point dipole be characterized by a dipole moment p_i.
2. Let R_i be a vector from the source point to the field point (**0**)

$$R_i = -x_i \boldsymbol{i} - y_i \boldsymbol{j}$$

$$|R_i| = (x_i^2 + y_i^2)^{\frac{1}{2}}. \tag{31}$$

3.   Define α_i as the angle between the z-axis and the line of action of $\boldsymbol{p}_i$.

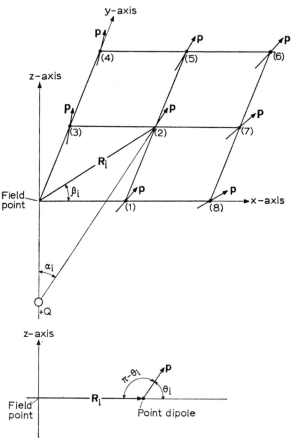

Fig. 44. Analysis of discrete dipole array with axis of rotation at center of dipole

4.   Define β_i as the angle between the x-axis and R_i.

The electric field intensity E_i, due to a point dipole is given [2]) by

$$E_i(r) = \frac{1}{4\pi\varepsilon_0}\left[\frac{3(r-r_i)}{|r-r_i|^5}\cdot p_i(r-r_i) - \frac{p_i}{|r-r_i|^3}\right] \tag{32}$$

where

$$r - r_i = R_i. \tag{33}$$

Resolving p_i into components yields

$$p_i = p_i[\sin \alpha_i \cos \beta_i \mathbf{i} + \sin \alpha_i \sin \beta_i \mathbf{j} + \cos \alpha_i \mathbf{k}] \tag{34}$$

where p_i is the absolute magnitude of the dipole moment and

$$\sin \alpha_i = \frac{R_i}{(R_i^2 + z^2)^{\frac{1}{2}}} \tag{35}$$

$$\cos \alpha_i = \frac{z}{(R_i^2 + z^2)^{\frac{1}{2}}} \tag{36}$$

$$\sin \beta_i = y_i/R_i \tag{37}$$

$$\cos \beta_i = x_i/R_i. \tag{38}$$

Using eqs. (31, 34, 35) and (36–38) and taking the dot product of $p \cdot R_i$ gives

$$p \cdot R_i = -p \left[\frac{x_i^2}{(R_i^2 + z^2)^{\frac{1}{2}}} + \frac{y_i^2}{(R_i^2 + z^2)^{\frac{1}{2}}} \right]. \tag{39}$$

Resolving $E_i(0)$ into components from eq. (32) and summing each one of the components over i from $i = 1 \rightarrow 8$, the field is obtained at $\mathbf{0}$ from all eight dipoles by use of eqs. (39) and (31):

$$E_x = \frac{p}{2\pi\varepsilon_0} \sum_{i=1}^{8} \frac{x_i}{(x_i^2 + y_i^2 + z^2)^{\frac{1}{2}}(x_i^2 + y_i^2)^{\frac{3}{2}}} \tag{40}$$

$$E_y = \frac{p}{2\pi\varepsilon_0} \sum_{i=1}^{8} \frac{y_i}{(x_i^2 + y_i^2 + z^2)^{\frac{1}{2}}(x_i^2 + y_i^2)^{\frac{3}{2}}} \tag{41}$$

$$E_z = -\frac{p}{2\pi\varepsilon_0} \sum_{i=1}^{8} \frac{zl}{(x_i^2 + y_i^2 + z^2)^{\frac{1}{2}}(x_i^2 + y_i^2)^{\frac{3}{2}}}. \tag{42}$$

CASE 3 (see fig. 45)

Using a similar analysis to that given in case 1 and taking into account the fixed positive end of each dipole, the components of $(E_i)_+$ and $(E_i)_-$ are resolved and summed over i ($i = 1 \rightarrow 8$):

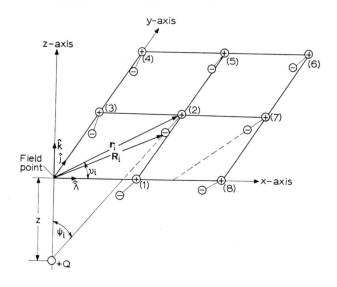

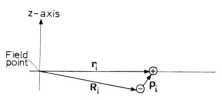

Fig. 45. Analysis of discrete dipole array with axis of rotation at fixed positive end

$$(E_x)_+ = - \frac{q}{4\pi\varepsilon_0} \sum_{i=1}^{8} \frac{x_i}{(x_i^2 + y_i^2)^{\frac{3}{2}}} \tag{43}$$

$$(E_y)_+ = - \frac{q}{4\pi\varepsilon_0} \sum_{i=1}^{8} \frac{y_i}{(x_i^2 + y_i^2)^{\frac{3}{2}}} \tag{44}$$

$$(E_z)_+ = 0 \tag{45}$$

$$(E_x)_- = \frac{q}{4\pi\varepsilon_0} \sum_{i=1}^{8} \frac{x_i \left(1 - \dfrac{l}{(x_i^2 + y_i^2 + z^2)^{\frac{1}{2}}}\right)}{\left[x_i^2 + y_i^2 - \dfrac{2l(x_i^2 + y_i^2)}{(x_i^2 + y_i^2 + z^2)^{\frac{1}{2}}} + l^2\right]^{\frac{3}{2}}} \tag{46}$$

$$(E_y)_- = \frac{q}{4\pi\varepsilon_0} \sum_{i=1}^{8} \frac{y_i \left(1 - \dfrac{l}{(x_i^2 + y_i^2 + z^2)^{\frac{1}{2}}}\right)}{\left[x_i^2 + y_i^2 - \dfrac{2l(x_i^2 + y_i^2)}{(x_i^2 + y_i^2 + z^2)^{\frac{1}{2}}} + l^2\right]^{\frac{3}{2}}} \tag{47}$$

$$(E_z)_- = -\frac{q}{4\pi\varepsilon_0} \sum_{i=1}^{8} \frac{\dfrac{zl}{(x_i^2 + y_i^2 + z^2)^{\frac{1}{2}}}}{\left[x_i^2 + y_i^2 - \dfrac{2l(x_i^2 + y_i^2)}{(x_i^2 + y_i^2 + z^2)^{\frac{1}{2}}} + l^2\right]^{\frac{3}{2}}} \cdot \tag{48}$$

B. The object of this second analysis is to determine the electric field intensity on the axis of symmetry of a uniform *discrete* dipole distribution assuming a charge separation on the dipole and a complete alignment of the dipoles to the field point. Thus it is necessary to find the field at point $(0, 0, z)$, assuming that the dipoles align with their negative tips towards $(0, 0, z)$ while their positive ends are held fixed.

Definitions:

1. Let $r_{mn} = mai + naj$ ($n, m = -20, \ldots, 0, 1 \ldots, 20$)   (49)

which locates dipole mn (see fig. 46).

2. Let a be the interdipole distance in a distribution of 41×41 dipoles (1681 dipoles).

3. Define l_{mn} as a vector from the negative charge of the (m, n) dipole to the positive charge of the (m, n) dipole.

Dividing the analysis into two parts the field at $(0, 0, z)$ is determined first by the positive charges. If $(E_{mn})_+$ is the field from the positive charge of the mn dipole, then

$$(E_{mn})_+ = \frac{q}{4\pi\varepsilon_0} \frac{(+\varrho_{mn})}{(\varrho_{mn})^3} \cdot \tag{50}$$

Solving for (ϱ_{mn}) from the following conditions

$$r_{mn} + \varrho_{mn} = -zk \tag{51}$$

and

$$\varrho_{mn} = -mai - naj - zk \tag{52}$$

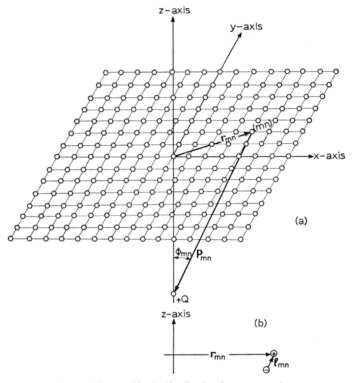

Fig. 46. Discrete dipole distribution in a square sheet

we obtain

$$\varrho_{mn} = [(ma)^2 + (na)^2 + (z)^2]^{\frac{1}{2}}. \tag{53}$$

When $(E_{mn})_+$ is resolved into components and summed, after substituting eq. (53) into (50), yields

$$(E_x)_+ = -\frac{qa}{4\pi\varepsilon_0} \sum_{m=-20}^{+20} \sum_{n=-20}^{+20} \frac{m}{[(ma)^2 + (na)^2 + z^2]^{\frac{3}{2}}} \tag{54}$$

$$(E_y)_+ = -\frac{qa}{4\pi\varepsilon_0} \sum_{m=-20}^{+20} \sum_{n=-20}^{+20} \frac{n}{[(ma)^2 + (na)^2 + z^2]^{\frac{3}{2}}} \tag{55}$$

$$(E_z)_+ = -\frac{qz}{4\pi\varepsilon_0} \sum_{m=-20}^{+20} \sum_{n=-20}^{+20} \frac{1}{[(ma)^2 + (na)^2 + z^2]^{\frac{3}{2}}}. \tag{56}$$

In a similar manner, the field of the negative charges of the *mn* dipoles may be resolved to yield

$$(E_x)_- = \frac{qa}{4\pi\varepsilon_0} \sum_{m=-20}^{+20} \sum_{n=-20}^{+20} \frac{m\left[1 - \frac{1}{[(ma)^2+(na)^2+z^2]^{\frac{1}{2}}}\right]}{[\sqrt{(ma)^2+(na)^2+z^2}-1]^3} \tag{57}$$

$$(E_y)_- = \frac{qa}{4\pi\varepsilon_0} \sum_{m=-20}^{+20} \sum_{n=-20}^{+20} \frac{n\left[1 - \frac{1}{[(ma)^2+(na)^2+z^2]^{\frac{1}{2}}}\right]}{[\sqrt{(ma)^2+(na)^2+z^2}-1]^3} \tag{58}$$

$$(E_z)_- = \frac{qz}{4\pi\varepsilon_0} \sum_{m=-20}^{+20} \sum_{n=-20}^{+20} \frac{1 - \frac{1}{[(ma)^2+(na)^2+z^2]^{\frac{1}{2}}}}{[\sqrt{(ma)^2+(na)^2+z^2}-1]^3}. \tag{59}$$

Thus the total field components at point $(0, 0, z)$ are

$$E_x = (E_x)_+ + (E_x)_- \tag{60}$$

$$E_y = (E_y)_+ + (E_y)_- \tag{61}$$

$$E_z = (E_z)_+ + (E_z)_-. \tag{62}$$

3 Discussion

Eqs. (21–30), (40–42) and (43–48) were programmed for the IBM 1620 computer and representative values of the three cases are given in table 1. For the point dipole case, eq. (32) represents the first two terms of a series expansion [2]). However, a more rigorous and more exact method (using more terms of the expansion) is available and is to be published at a later time, taking into account more accurate evaluations of the field. The two methods stated above yield values which are very close.

From the results given in table 1, it is observed that the point dipole provides a poor approximation to the lecithin molecule; i.e. the *x* and *y* field components in case 2 are in the positive direction, whereas in case 3, they are in the negative direction.

The correlation between cases 1 and 2 is much better. The direction and magnitude of the field components are in much better agreement.

TABLE 1

Electric field values for cases 1, 2 and 3

(All values must be multiplied by 10^{10})

Field	Dipole (1)	Dipole (2)	Dipole (3)	Dipole (4)	Dipole (5)	Dipole (6)	Dipole (7)	Dipole (8)	$\sum\limits_{i=1}^{8}(E)_i$
$(E_x)_+$	−4.312	−1.621	0	0	−0.4216	−0.4253	−0.8523	−1.183	−8.820
$(E_x)_-$	4.545	1.715	0	0	0.4516	0.4509	0.9033	1.254	9.318
E_x	0.2327	0.0934	0	0	0.0255	0.0256	0.0509	0.0703	0.4985
$(E_y)_+$	0	−1.621	−4.312	−1.183	−0.8523	−0.4253	−0.4216	0	−8.820
$(E_y)_-$	0	1.715	4.545	1.254	0.9033	0.4509	0.4516	0	9.318
E_y	0	0.0934	0.2327	0.0703	0.0509	0.0256	0.0255	0	0.4985
$(E_z)_+$	−1.274	−0.4782	−1.274	−0.1741	−0.1252	−0.0622	−0.1252	−0.1741	−3.687
$(E_z)_-$	−1.383	−0.5211	−1.383	−0.1901	−0.1367	−0.679	−0.1367	−0.1901	−4.009
E_z	−2.657	−0.9993	−2.657	−0.3642	−0.2619	−0.1302	−0.2619	−0.3642	−7.696
E_x	0.3017	0.1065	0	0	0.0269	0.0264	0.0538	0.07512	0.5904
E_y	0	0.1065	0.3017	0.0751	0.0538	0.0264	0.0269	0	0.5904
E_z	−6.033	−2.131	−6.033	−0.7511	−0.5374	−0.2643	−0.5374	−0.7511	−15.121
$(E_x)_+$	−5.036	−1.779	0	0	−0.4450	−0.4352	−0.9003	−1.259	−9.866
$(E_x)_-$	3.293	1.457	0	0	0.4287	0.4212	0.4288	1.167	7.215
E_x	−1.745	−0.3224	0	0	−0.0215	−0.0141	−0.4716	−0.0923	−2.651
$(E_y)_+$	0	−1.779	−5.036	−1.259	−0.9003	−0.4352	−0.4450	0	−9.866
$(E_y)_-$	0	1.457	3.293	1.167	0.4288	0.4212	0.4287	0	7.215
E_y	0	−0.3224	−1.745	−0.0923	−0.4716	−0.0141	−0.0215	0	−2.651
$(E_z)_+$	0	0	0	0	0	0	0	0	0
$(E_z)_-$	−2.035	−0.8992	−2.035	−0.3593	−0.2637	−0.1351	−0.2637	−0.3593	−6.346
E_z	−2.035	−0.8992	−2.035	−0.3593	−0.2637	−0.1351	−0.2637	−0.3593	−6.346

This is to be expected since the center of charge remains in the same position in both cases.

If point dipoles are to be utilized in representing the lecithin molecule, modifications in the model are necessary. Thus

1. The point dipoles can be translated vertically downward 1.5 Å, so that they coincide with the centers of charge of the lecithin molecule.
2. A nearest neighbour type approximation may be used around the field point (i.e. dumbell type dipoles, as used in case 3, may be substituted for the point dipoles over a limited vicinity around the field point).

From the analysis in part B of the field on an axis of symmetry, where the dipoles are considered *discrete*, eqs. (54) through (62) have been programmed for an IBM 1620 and 7044. The results indicate that, at distances greater than 5 Å from the distributions, the percentage difference between discrete and continuous approaches are negligible.

In order to have a comparison to the dipole sheets, the field on an axis of symmetry underneath a fixed charged sheet has been derived in chapter 2. In that derivation, a homogeneous charge distribution was assumed, and an integration process allowed for the evaluation of the field. (Thus the charge density σ = charge/unit area.) By using an alternative method of a summation procedure (rather than the above integration method) the specific location of the charges could be taken into account to determine the field. Thus, the above two methods were programmed on an IBM 1620 to determine the percent difference calculated in the field values between the discrete and homogeneous charge distributions. Representative values are given in table 2. Once again, the percentage difference between the two approaches becomes negligible at distances greater than 5 Å.

The final problem to be considered involves finding the percent difference in the field between the discrete and point dipole treatment of a large finite distribution considering only the field in the plane of the dipoles. (Always assuming that the dipoles align to a field point normal to the plane.) The field for the *point dipole case* has been treated in chapter 5. From part B of the derivations section, modifications of eqs. (54) through (62) may be utilized for the discrete dipole case. Programming these equations from these two cases for the IBM 1620 yields field values comparable to those obtained in part A.

TABLE 2

z (Å)	E_z (newton/coulomb) for a discrete charge distribution	E_z (newton/coulomb) for a homogeneous charge sheet	Percent difference
1	1.68812×10^{10}	3.55362×10^{10}	52.495
2	2.73153×10^{10}	3.48854×10^{10}	21.699
3	3.16177×10^{10}	3.42359×10^{10}	7.647
4	3.27619×10^{10}	3.35882×10^{10}	2.460
5	3.26964×10^{10}	3.29432×10^{10}	0.749
6	3.2236×10^{10}	3.23013×10^{10}	0.215
7	3.16463×10^{10}	3.16632×10^{10}	0.053

From the above discussion, the following conclusions may be drawn:

1. The point dipole representation for model systems is an excellent approximation to cholesterol type molecules.

2. Slight modifications are needed for the point dipole treatment if it is to represent adequately lecithin and fatty acid molecules. However, the modifications are slight and easily handled and do not detract from the usefulness of the point dipole approach.

3. A comparison of the field on an axis of symmetry normal to a sheet of either discrete or point dipoles indicates that the point dipole representation is adequate and almost identical to the more laboriously calculated discrete case.

4. Representations of fixed charged distributions using an integration procedure or the more laborious summation procedure are almost identical. The integration procedures described in chapters 1–5 are simpler and allow for closed form solutions.

5. A further comparison of the field normal to a large distribution of point dipoles or discrete dipoles indicates that rigor and accuracy are not sacrificed by the use of point dipoles. The two cases are almost identical.

4 Summary

Derivations and computer analyses of the electric field intensity for modifications of dipole and charged sheets evaluated in the plane of the distribution and normal to the distribution are presented. A comparison of the results of the derivations and analyses for the point dipoles and point charges are in almost all instances equivalent to the discrete approach. In the one exception of the representation of the lecithin molecule, minor modification of the point dipole treatment offers a convenient means of allowing the simpler, closed form solutions to be utilized. Thus it is concluded that the findings described in chapters 1–5 utilizing the fixed point dipole and point charge approach are considered accurate for this first approximation.

5 References

[1] Huang, C., Wheeldon, L., Thompson, T. E., J. Mol. Biol. **8** [1] (1964) 148.
[2] Reitz, J. R., Milford, F. J., *Foundations of electromagnetic theory* (Addison-Wesley Publ. Co., Reading, Mass., 1962) p. 37.

Chapter 7

An electrostatic self-consistent field analysis of a simulated biological membrane

Contents

1 *Introduction*

A three component system consisting of representations of a lipid mono-layer structure, an adjacent protein monolayer and an environmental macromolecule simulating a segment of a biological membrane are analyzed from a self-consistent electrostatic field point of view. Based on a longitudinal section of half the unit membrane as conceived in the Danielli model of the "pauci bimolecular lipid leaflet" (see figs. 1, 2 and 47), the influence of cholesterol in the lipid layer is determined by a

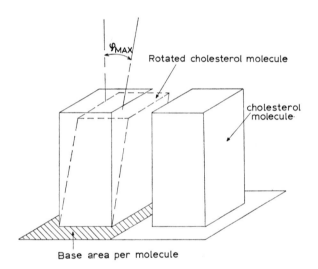

Fig. 47. Limitation on the rotation of cholesterol molecules

series of quasi electrostatic calculations. By assuming the lipid matrix to be entirely composed of cholesterol molecules of a sheet 1.4×10^3 square Å (a square 37.95 by 37.95 Å), the polar hydroxyl group of each molecule may be represented as a point dipole. These polar groups are allowed to orient themselves within an allowed specified angle in the direction of the electric fields originating in the adjacent protein layer and charged macromolecule, as well as fields generated within the cholesterol layer itself. When the dipoles orient to an equilibrium position, the electric field intensity may then be determined in the lipid layer as well as any arbitrary point adjacent to the layer.

The specifications for this model system have been obtained from monolayer studies and protein chemistry experiments. Each cholesterol molecule will occupy a right rectangular prism, having a base of surface area of 40 Å² (from force area curve measurements of monolayers), shaped as a square, and a height of 20 Å. Since this layer represents a condensed phase each square is fixed in the sense that translational motion is not permitted. In the center of each square, perpendicular to the sheet, lies an idealized cholesterol molecule which can rotate freely about the z-axis. However, any angle θ measured from the z-axis must remain less than a maximum θ_M. This angle θ_M is obtained by considering bond angles and the geometry of the system. (This angle is found to be approximately 10 degrees.) Another condition imposed on θ is restricted rotation

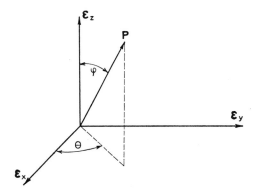

Fig. 48. Dipole orientation

between θ and θ_M. This internal resistance to twisting of the polar group is due to an opposing torque $g(\theta)$. The original orientation of each dipole is also subject to the condition that $0 < \theta < \theta_M$. Specific θ's and φ's for each dipole are determined with the aid of a programmed random number generator. The angles generated are then weighted, such that a large number of original orientations of θ fall in the approximate range of $0 < \theta < \frac{3}{4}\theta_M$ rather than $\frac{3}{4}\theta_M < \theta < \theta_M$. The weighting factor is introduced to simulate the physical probability that, statistically speaking, more cholesterol molecules are oriented near 0° than near θ_M° (see fig. 48).

Only the electrostatic field interactions of this system are considered. The dipole moment of the polar group of the cholesterol molecule is

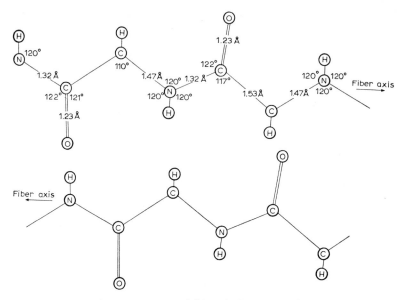

Fig. 49. Structure of β-keratin fibrous protein

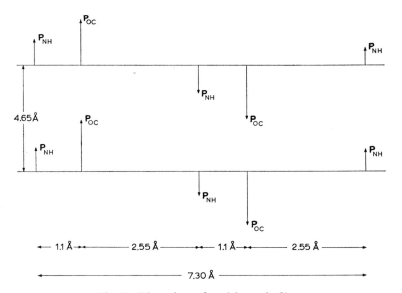

Fig. 50. Dimensions of model protein fibers

assigned the value of 2.01 debye based on dielectric studies. The field from this monolayer of dipoles will approximate very closely the field from a bilayer of dipoles as will be shown in chapter 8.

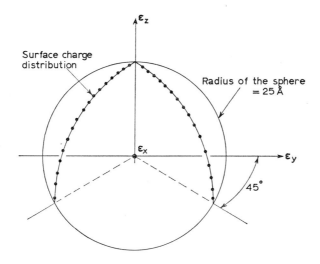

Model ovalbumin molecule

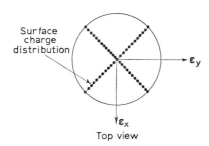

Top view

Fig. 51. Model ovalbumin molecule

The protein monolayer forms a ten to fifteen angström thick molecular envelope that shields the lipid phase. The existence of such a protein component in natural membranes is based upon surface tension studies. The observation that living cells in an aqueous phase have very low solubilities and surface tensions (≈ 0.1 dyne/cm) has led to the hypothesis of a protein lipid membrane. The protein itself is an unfolded and uncoiled "fabric protein" assumed to be in an extended β-conformation. The fabric is arranged in a pleated type sheet. Compared to an α helix configuration, this permits a more effective interaction of the peptide bonds with the lipid head groups, thus allowing a greater degree of penetration of non-polar side chains into the lipids' non-polar region. The detailed specifications of this protein structure may be found in the original work of Pauling, Cory and Branson [1]). In this model, each acid is represented by two point dipoles, the C=O (2.5 debye) and NH (1.31 debye) having the largest moments. The dipoles are fixed and non-rotating and are pleated on a sheet comparable in size to the lipid array. There are ten amino acid residues per fiber and eight protein fibers. (See figs. 49, 50.)

The environmental macromolecules have been chosen to simulate naturally occurring protein molecules with large dipole moments (e.g. ovalbumin; Smythe [2]). The model consists of 105 charges distributed over the surface of a 25 Å radius sphere. There are 78 negative and 27 positive electronic charges with a net negative charge of 51. The charges are distributed on two rings. Ring 1, at 45°, has a net charge of -52 and ring 2 at 135° of $+1$. The dipole moment of this model is calculated to be 119 debye. (See fig. 51.)

2 *Theory*

2.1 *Electric field in the lipid layer*

The purpose here is to derive, through a self-consistent field analysis, an equilibrium orientation in space for each dipole moment vector of the lipid array. This involves the solution of a set of three simultaneous equations. The first equation of the set determines the summed electric field $E(r)$ at a field point located by a vector r from (1) the fields $E_l(r)$ of the swinging dipoles in the lipid layer, (2) the fields $E_p(r)$ from the fixed dipoles in the protein layer and (3) the field $E_m(r)$ from the environmental macromolecule:

$$E(r) = E_l(r) + E_p(r) + E_m(r). \tag{1}$$

The second equation of the set relates the external torque M on a dipole to the dipole moment p and the electric field $E(r)$ at each dipole in the lipid layer. These dipoles are not free to translate but may rotate. The external torque M forces p to rotate such that it will align with the electric field $E(r)$, and assume a zero torque orientation:

$$M = p \times E(r). \tag{2}$$

The third equation of this set expresses an equilibrium condition between the external torque M and an internal resisting rotational torque $g(\theta)$

$$M = g(\theta). \tag{3}$$

The first two terms of eq. (1) may be expanded by the general expressions commonly utilized for point dipoles (see section 6.1 below). $E_m(r)$ in eq. (1) expresses the electric field at r due to an environmental macromolecule located by p_m. This part of the electrostatic field equation may be put in the form of a multipole series expansion which has the advantage of providing accurate answers when the source charges are a set of discretely located point sources. Thus

$$E_m(r) = E_0(r) + E_1(r) + E_2(r). \tag{4}$$

Expanding

$$E_0(r) = \frac{1}{4\pi\varepsilon_0} \frac{1}{|h|^3} \sum_i^n e_i h \tag{5}$$

where h is the distance from the origin to the field point, e_i is the ith electronic charge of the macromolecule's distribution, and i is the running index, $i = 1, \ldots, n$, where n is the number of electronic charges of the distribution.

$$E_1(r) = \frac{1}{4\pi\varepsilon_0} \left[\frac{3(p_m \cdot h)h}{|h|^5} - \frac{p_m}{|h|^3} \right] \tag{6}$$

where p_m is the dipole moment of the charge distribution and

$$E_2(r) = \frac{1}{4\pi\varepsilon_0} (E_{mx}\hat{\imath} + E_{my}\hat{\jmath} + E_{mz}\hat{k}) \tag{7}$$

where E_{mx}, E_{my} and E_{mz} are the field components of the quadrupole term in tensor notation (see section 6.1 below for expansion of terms).

Eq. (2) may be expanded in the form

$$M = |p||E(r)|[(E_z \sin \theta \sin \phi - E_y \cos \theta)\hat{\imath} + (E_x \cos \theta - E_z \sin \theta \cos \phi)\hat{\jmath}$$
$$+ (E_y \sin \theta \cos \phi - E_x \sin \theta \sin \phi)\hat{k}] \quad (8)$$

where M is the external torque, p is the dipole moment of cholesterol, $E(r)$ is the electrostatic field at r, E_x, E_y, and E_z are the components of the unit vector $\hat{E}$ of field $E(r)$. The angles θ and φ describe the orientation of $\hat{E}$ when φ is measured in the x, y-plane.

In eq. (3) $g(\theta)$ is a general, adjustable representation of the "stiffness" of a rotating p. This concept is illustrated by

$$g(\theta) = C_1\theta + C_2\theta^2 + \ldots + C_n\theta^n \quad (9)$$

$$C_1 = C_3 = C_5 = \ldots = C_n = 0$$

$$g(\theta) = C_0 \tan k\theta$$

$$C_0, C_1, \ldots, k = \text{constants.} \quad (10)$$

The intersection of $g(\theta)$ and $|M|$ given as a function of θ from eq. (8) defines a θ and hence, the dipoles' orientation with respect to the axis.

Physically, the external torque M is a function of θ and φ while $g(\theta)$ is independent of p. However, there is no internal resisting torque acting on a change in φ, so the dipole freely aligns with the same angle φ as $E(r)$.

The three simultaneous equations (1), (2) and (3), have been solved on a 7044 IBM computer by utilizing an iterative technique until a stable condition is reached. The output from one iteration is a set of two angles θ and φ for each dipole in the array. These angles define the orientation of p and are used as input into the next iteration. The dipole array has stabilized when the difference between the output from iteration m and $m+1$ for each dipole is arbitrarily small. The original values of θ and φ for each p are randomly generated and weighted. Successive values of θ and φ are found for a dipole by choosing its location as a field point located by r and summing the electric fields from all the sources at that point, finding the torque on each dipole, and solving the torque equilibrium equation. This is repeated for each dipole in the array for each iteration.

2.2 *Electric field at an arbitrary point*

To determine the field at an arbitrary point, a similar set of equations is utilized as in § 2.1. The modified equations involve an *ra* distance vector from the origin of the *x*, *y*-coordinate system, locating an *arbitrary field point*. These modifications and the corresponding equations are given in section 6.2 below.

3 *Discussion*

To extrapolate the electrostatic role of cholesterol in a biological membrane segment, the lipid layer has been formed in this membrane model

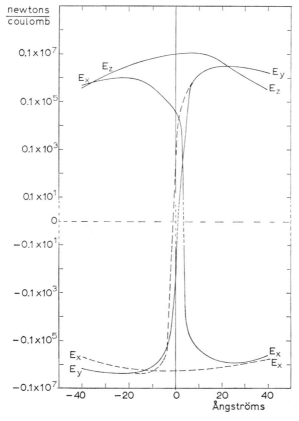

Fig. 52. Field graphs for a macromolecule at $z = 30$ Å

entirely from cholesterol molecules. The lipid protein system is considered to be the source of the electric field although it is corrected for the presence of a charge bearing macromolecule. Thus, one may consider a time in a membrane's history when it is in a formative stage (the P.P.L.O.

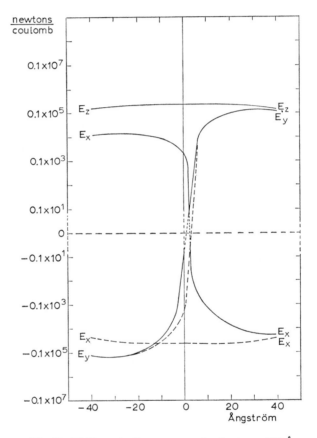

Fig. 53. Field graphs for a macromolecule at $z = 100$ Å

(smallest living organism) has a surface area of 7.5×10^5 Å^2 whereas this system is 1.4×10^3 Å^2) or possibly breaking into smaller segments, such that a neighbouring macromolecule will be influenced by the electro-statics of this lipid protein system. The electric field from this macromolecule will then effect the orienting of the dipoles of the lipid layer.

This field contribution then corrects the lipid protein field in which the macromolecule is embedded. The magnitude and direction of the self-consistent electrostatic force acting on the macromolecule can then be determined.

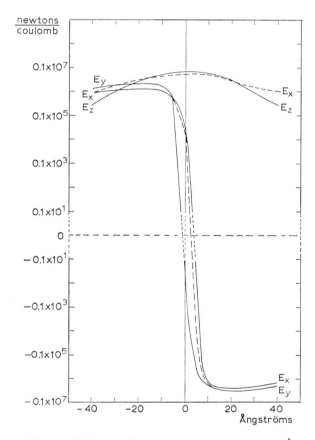

Fig. 54. Field graphs for a macromolecule at $z = -30$ Å

Three cases have been considered for three different locations of the macromolecule. When $z = 30$ Å and $z = 100$ Å, the macromolecule is positioned between the bilayer structure of the membrane. When $z = -30$ Å, the macromolecule is positioned adjacent to the membrane structure within the cell. The coordinates in the yz-plane at $x = 0$ chosen for the graphs 1–3 are given in figs. 52–54. Two orientations of dipoles in the protein layer are considered on these graphs. When $\Omega = 0$ (unbroken line) the dipoles of the protein layer lie parallel to the plane of the lipid layer. When $\Omega = 90$ (broken line) the dipoles of the protein lie perpendicular to the lipid plane. Data for other locations of the macromolecule, the use of different constraining functions $g(\theta)$, the field values *in* the lipid layer, the computer programs and data, and more complete details of this system may be found in the original thesis [3]).

4 Conclusions

Aside from the measure of high force fields positioned in the domain, these analyses show a number of interesting characteristics. The symmetry of force fields provides a clue to the mechanism associated with membrane pores. For $z = -30$ Å and $z = +30$ Å the E_z components are almost identical. Thus, small differences on either side of the protein–lipid layer could create an imbalance allowing strong forces to play a major part in transport phenomena. In other respects, these force fields show abrupt changes in sign throughout the x or y-plane. It can be calculated that E_x or E_y change sign rapidly as they cross the y-axis. The attractive or repulsive forces on a charged molecule due to such sign reversal, may well be involved in the selection and ordering processes near the membrane.

It may be observed in comparing this system with other kinds of lipid systems, that the specific characteristics of cholesterol in the lipid layer do not alter the electrogenic properties of the membrane. Calculations for other types of molecules in the membrane have indicated similar force fields. It is therefore concluded that if there are unique and unusual functions of cholesterol in the membrane structure, they do not reside in its electrostatic properties.

Finally, this self-consistent electrostatic field approach offers a unique method for evaluating the electrogenic properties of models simulating biological membranes.

5 Summary

A three component system consisting of representations of a lipid monolayer structure, an adjacent protein monolayer and an environmental macromolecule, simulating a segment of a biological membrane are analyzed from a self-consistent electrostatic point of view. The role of cholesterol in the lipid layer is considered in terms of its electrogenic properties. A possible mechanism for pore formation and transport phenomena as well as ordering and selecting characteristics of charged molecules near the membrane are established. High field values in and around the membrane are confirmed. The electrostatic self-consistent field approach offers a unique method to evaluate the electrogenic properties of model systems simulating biological membranes.

6 Appendix

6.1 Point dipole field expressions

For eq. (1) in the lipid layer

$$E_l(r) = \frac{1}{4\pi\varepsilon_0} \sum_{j=1}^{NSP} \left[\frac{3\boldsymbol{p} \cdot (\boldsymbol{r}-\boldsymbol{r}_j)}{|r-r'_j|}(r-r'_j) - \frac{\boldsymbol{p}}{|r-r'_j|^3} \right] \tag{11}$$

where $E_l(r)$ expresses the field at r, due to the sum of the fields from the swinging dipoles in the lipid layer, i.e., the xy-plane, $\boldsymbol{p}$ is the dipole moment of the lipid molecules, r and r' locate field and source points respectively; and both lie in the xy-plane and NSP are the number of source dipoles in the lipid layer.

$$E_p(r) = \frac{1}{4\pi\varepsilon_0} \sum_{\alpha} \left[\frac{3\boldsymbol{pp}_k \cdot (\boldsymbol{t}-\boldsymbol{t}'_\alpha)}{|t-t'_\alpha|}(t-t'_\alpha) - \frac{\boldsymbol{pp}_k}{|t-t'_\alpha|^3} \right] \tag{12}$$

where $k = 1, 2$; $\boldsymbol{pp}_k$, $k = 1$, is the dipole moment of the C=O bond, $\boldsymbol{pp}_k$, $k = 2$, is the dipole moment of the NH bond, t and t' locate field and source points respectively; t' lies in the ab-plane and t is a function of vector r.

Expansion of the quadrupole terms in equation 7

$$\begin{aligned}
E_{mx} = &- \left\{ Q_{xx} \frac{1}{2} \left[\frac{4d}{h^5} - \frac{5d}{h^7}(3d^2 - h^2) \right] + Q_{yy} \frac{1}{2} \left[-\frac{2d}{h^5} - \frac{5d}{h^7}(3f^2 - h^2) \right] \right. \\
&+ Q_{zz} \frac{1}{2} \left[-\frac{2d}{h^5} - \frac{5d}{h^7}(3g^2 - h^2) \right] + Q_{xy} 3 \left(\frac{f}{h^5} - \frac{5d^2 f}{h^7} \right) \\
&\left. + Q_{xz} 3 \left(\frac{g}{h^5} - \frac{5d^2 g}{h^7} \right) + Q_{yz} 3 \left(-\frac{5dfg}{h^7} \right) \right\}
\end{aligned} \tag{13}$$

$$E_{my} = - \left\{ Q_{xx} \frac{1}{2} \left[-\frac{2f}{h^5} - \frac{5f}{h^7}(3d^2 - h^2) \right] + Q_{yy} \frac{1}{2} \left[\frac{4f}{h^5} - \frac{5f}{h^7}(3f^2 - h^2) \right] \right.$$

$$+ Q_{zz} \frac{1}{2} \left[-\frac{2f}{h^5} - \frac{5f}{h^7}(3g^2 - h^2) \right] + Q_{xy} 3 \left(\frac{d}{h^5} - \frac{5df^2}{h^7} \right) + Q_{xz} 3 \left(-\frac{5dfg}{h^7} \right)$$

$$\left. + Q_{yz} 3 \left(\frac{g}{h^5} - \frac{5f^2 g}{h^7} \right) \right\} \tag{14}$$

$$E_{mz} = - \left\{ Q_{xx} \frac{1}{2} \left[-\frac{2g}{h^5} - \frac{5g}{h^7}(3d^2 - h^2) \right] + Q_{yy} \frac{1}{2} \left[\frac{2g}{h^5} - \frac{5g}{h^7}(3f^2 - h^2) \right] \right.$$

$$+ Q_{zz} \frac{1}{2} \left[+\frac{2g}{h^5} - \frac{5g}{h^7}(3g^2 - h^2) \right] + Q_{yz} 3 \left(\frac{f}{h^5} - \frac{5fg^2}{h^7} \right)$$

$$\left. + Q_{yz} 3 \left(\frac{d}{h^5} - \frac{5dg^2}{h^7} \right) + Q_{yz} 3 \left(\frac{f}{h^5} - \frac{5fg^2}{h^7} \right) \right\} \tag{15}$$

where h is the distance from the *dfg* coordinate system origin to the field point and $Q_{xx}, Q_{yy}, \ldots, Q_{yz}$ are the components of the symmetric quadrupole moment tensor.

Derivations for eqs. (5–8), and (13–15) are given in the original thesis [3]).

6.2 *Electric field at an arbitrary point*

The equations for the electrostatic field from (1) the layer of stabilized lipid dipoles, (2) the layer of protein dipoles and (3) the environmental macromolecule, *at an arbitrary field point*, are similar to eqs. (11), (12) and (4):

$$E_l(r_a) = \frac{1}{4\pi\varepsilon_0} \sum_{j=1}^{NSP} \left[\frac{3p \cdot (r_a - r_j)}{|r_a - r_j'|^5}(r_a - r_j') - \frac{p}{(r_a - r_j')^3} \right] \tag{16}$$

(the field from the layer of stabilized lipid dipoles at an arbitrary point) where r_a is a vector from the origin of the *xyz*-coordinate system locating an arbitrary field point.

$$E_p(r_a) = \frac{1}{4\pi\varepsilon_0} \sum_{\alpha} \left[\frac{3pp_k \cdot (r_a - rp_\alpha')}{|r_a - rp_\alpha'|^5}(r_a - rp_\alpha') - \frac{pp_k}{|r_a - rp_\alpha'|^3} \right] \tag{17}$$

(the field from the layer of protein dipoles at an arbitrary point) where r_a is defined above and rp is a vector which locates the pp_k source dipole in the protein layer with respect to the *xyz*-origin.

$$E_m(r_a) = E_0(r_a) + E_1(r_a) + E_2(r_a) \qquad (18)$$

(the field from the environmental macromolecule at an arbitrary field point) where *s* is a vector which locates the arbitrary field point with respect to the *dfg* coordinate system.

7 *References*

[1] Pauling, L., Cory, R., Branson, H., Proc. Natl. Acad. Sci. Washington **37** (1951) 205.

[2] McClellan, A. L., *Tables of experimental dipole moments* (Freeman, San Francisco, 1963) p. 551, 576.

[3] Gallucci, V., Dissertation (1966) State University of N. Y. at Buffalo, N. Y., Theoretical Biology Division, in partial fulfillment of the M. S. Degree.

SECTION III

Applications of a surface dipole model to biological cells

Chapter 8

Rationale

Contents

1 *Introduction*

In chapters 1–7, attention was focussed upon only the simplest components which constitute the necessary and essential molecular configurations of all membrane structures. Electron microscopists have shown [1]) that the backbone of all biological membranes is a bimolecular lipid layer. Surface scientists have shown that these lipid molecules must exist in a borderline state between solid and liquid phases with their polar end groups extending outward, normal to the plane of the lipid leaflet. In chapters 2–7, electrostatic considerations of this bilayer structure have dealt primarily with a single layer of dipoles which are allowed to rotate freely within the plane of the lipid layer, thus aligning themselves within the field of adjacent charged macromolecules. Such alignment of dipoles creates comparatively large force fields and this finding stimulated further efforts in this direction. Since all membranes show an over-all net charge, the field from a planar array of fixed charges has also been derived showing an equally large force field. Thus, it is not essential to this theory to explain these large force fields only by fixed charge phenomena. However, it is more reasonable to assume from chemical considerations, that both dipole and charge configurations exist in the membrane and that their fields add by superposition.

The rationale for studying dipole arrays rather than fixed charge arrays, is more fundamental than has been previously stated. It is the purpose of these studies to link known structural configurations of the membrane to functional mechanisms. The dipole layer of lipids is well characterized while a fixed charge configuration is more elusive. While each polar end group of a lipid molecule has the potential of ionizing, its exact state in the membrane at a given time is unknown. Therefore, it is far safer to consider the dipole structures as the origin of the force fields within the cell, with the realization that these may be minimum effects with the addition of field from fixed charge arrays.

In considering dipole arrays, two limitations of previous chapters must be kept in mind. The first limitation assumes that for every point in space, the dipoles of the array will realign and focus at each new point, creating a maximum force field at each new point in space being studied. This constant realignment of dipoles to plot the maximum force at each field point within the domain, is a useful technique however far removed it may appear at first glance from actual events. To show the reasonableness of this mechanism, this first section derives expressions for an array of dipoles aligned to a fixed field point, showing adjacent field points (within 500–1000 Å) still maintaining comparable high field values. Thus, it will be shown that complete realignment of dipoles to constantly changing field points, is an excellent approximation to the field under the dipole array when the dipoles are focused to any fixed field point. This establishes the validity of utilizing this technique of realignment of the dipoles to each new field point.

The second limitation involves the use of a single dipole layer instead of a bilayer of dipoles, back to back, in representing the naturally occurring biological case. Strong arguments have been put forth that a single layer of dipoles is a poor representation of a bilayer where the field of the second dipole layer may substantially subtract from the effect of the field of the single layer. Although the two layers of dipoles may be anywhere from 25 Å to 100 Å apart, separated by the lipid tails of the individual dipoles, it is difficult to see intuitively how the bilayer structure of dipoles would not measurably decrease the field. In order to clarify this point thoroughly, the second part of this chapter is devoted to deriving expressions based on a bilayer structure of dipoles. In addition, the bilayer of dipoles will be structured such that the individual dipoles do *not* have free rotation and are perpendicular to the membrane plane; a configuration which will yield a *minimum* electric field adjacent to it. It will be shown that the field values from these calculations, when compared to those of a single dipole layer, differ by slightly more than an order of magnitude. This establishes the usefulness of the "dipole aligned array" representation for considering maximum effects.

Other second and third order effects must be added to this model system to simulate other variables in the naturally occurring membrane. Such studies encompassing a protein monolayer and charged macromolecules as a part of the model system, have already been completed and relegated to second and third order influence (see chapter 7). The role of water molecules is considered in chapter 12.

It is, without question, the influence of the dipole surface or fixed charge surface of the membrane structure that gives rise to huge force fields within the cell, and this is of major biological significance. Studies attempting to explain cellular functions by mechanisms utilizing these force fields are well under way. Such basic mechanisms as (1) cell division, (2) specialized functions (secretion, nerve conduction etc.), and (3) an explanation of intercellular distances fall within this category. Of prime concern are the organizational characteristics within cells of diverse geometries based on the surface dipole model developed. Thus given any geometrical shaped cell, it is possible to map the force field contours within the cell originating from this dipole membrane model. These studies have now been completed and their *general properties* and interpretation of results are given in the latter part of this chapter.

2 *The non-aligned dipole case*

2.1 *Derivation*

The purpose here is to determine the equations for *E* at any point beneath a distribution of dipoles. It is assumed that the dipoles are free to rotate and align to an arbitrary point (not necessarily the field point). It is further assumed that the distribution is homogeneous and characterized by a dipole moment density *p* per unit area whose magnitude *p* is constant.

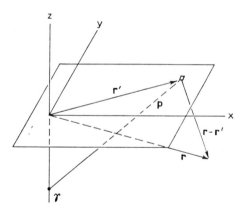

Fig. 55. Dipoles aligned to an arbitrary point not necessarily the field point

Referring to fig. 55, the origin of the coordinate system is chosen such that it lies in the plane of the distribution and that the point to which all dipoles are aligning lies on the *z*-axis. Letting

$$\mathbf{r'} = x'\mathbf{i} + y'\mathbf{j} \tag{1}$$

locate the source element dA', and

$$\mathbf{r} = x\mathbf{i} + y\mathbf{j} + z\mathbf{k} \tag{2}$$

locating the field point, then

$$\mathbf{r} - \mathbf{r'} = (x - x')\mathbf{i} + (y - y')\mathbf{j} + z\mathbf{k} \tag{3}$$

and

$$|\mathbf{r} - \mathbf{r'}| = [(x-x')^2 + (y-y')^2 + z^2]^{\frac{1}{2}}. \tag{4}$$

If the coordinates of the point to which all the dipoles align are $(0, 0, \gamma)$, and the magnitude of the dipole moment per unit area is a constant p, then it follows that

$$\mathbf{p}(x', y', \gamma) = p\hat{\mathbf{p}}(x', y', \gamma). \tag{5}$$

However

$$\hat{\mathbf{p}} = \frac{x'\hat{\mathbf{i}} + y'\hat{\mathbf{j}} - \gamma\hat{\mathbf{k}}}{[x'^2 + y'^2 + \gamma^2]^{\frac{1}{2}}} \tag{6}$$

so that

$$\hat{\mathbf{p}}(x', y', \gamma) = \frac{p(x'\hat{\mathbf{i}} + y'\hat{\mathbf{j}} - \gamma\hat{\mathbf{k}})}{[x'^2 + y'^2 + \gamma^2]^{\frac{1}{2}}}. \tag{7}$$

Performing the scalar product $\mathbf{p} \cdot (\mathbf{r} - \mathbf{r'})$ yields

$$\mathbf{p} \cdot (\mathbf{r} - \mathbf{r'}) = \frac{px'(x-x') + py'(y-y') - pz\gamma}{[x'^2 + y'^2 + \gamma^2]^{\frac{1}{2}}}. \tag{8}$$

Since the electric field intensity due to the element dA' is given by

$$d\mathbf{E} = -\nabla \left[\frac{\mathbf{p} \cdot (\mathbf{r} - \mathbf{r'})}{4\pi\varepsilon_0 |\mathbf{r} - \mathbf{r'}|^3} dA' \right] \tag{9}$$

where the gradient operates on field (unprimed) variables.

It is possible to determine $d\mathbf{E}$ by substituting eqs. (4) and (8) into (9)

$$d\mathbf{E} = -\frac{p}{4\pi\varepsilon_0} \nabla \left[\frac{x'(x-x') + y'(y-y') - z\gamma}{(x'^2 + y'^2 + \gamma^2)^{\frac{1}{2}}[(x-x')^2 + (y-y')^2 + z^2]^{\frac{3}{2}}} \right] dA'. \tag{10}$$

Performing the indicated operations (differentiating with respect to x for dE_x, with respect to y for dE_y and with respect to z for dE_z) and integrating over the entire distribution, yields the three components in integral form:

$$E_x(x, y, z, \gamma) = -\frac{p}{4\pi\varepsilon_0} \int_{x'=a}^{x'=b} \int_{y'=c}^{y'=d}$$

$$\times \frac{x'dx'dy'}{[(x-x')^2+(y-y')^2+z^2]^{\frac{3}{2}}(x'^2+y'^2+\gamma^2)^{\frac{1}{2}}}$$

$$+\frac{p}{4\pi\varepsilon_0} \int_{x'=a}^{x'=b} \int_{y'=c}^{y'=d}$$

$$\times \frac{3(x-x')[x'(x-x')+y'(y-y')-z\gamma]dx'dy'}{[(x-x')^2+(y-y')^2+z^2]^{\frac{5}{2}}(x'^2+y'^2+\gamma^2)^{\frac{1}{2}}} \quad (11)$$

$$E_y(x, y, z, \gamma) = -\frac{p}{4\pi\varepsilon_0} \int_{x'=a}^{x'=b} \int_{y'=c}^{y'=d}$$

$$\times \frac{y'dx'dy'}{[(x-x')^2+(y-y')^2+z^2]^{\frac{3}{2}}(x'^2+y'^2+\gamma^2)^{\frac{1}{2}}}$$

$$+\frac{p}{4\pi\varepsilon_0} \int_{x'=a}^{x'=b} \int_{y'=c}^{y'=d}$$

$$\times \frac{3(y-y')[x'(x-x')+y'(y-y')-z\gamma]dx'dy'}{[(x-x')^2+(y-y')^2+z^2]^{\frac{5}{2}}(x'^2+y'^2+\gamma^2)^{\frac{1}{2}}} \quad (12)$$

$$E_z(x, y, z, \gamma) = +\frac{p}{4\pi\varepsilon_0} \int_{x'=a}^{x'=b} \int_{y'=c}^{y'=d}$$

$$\times \frac{\gamma dx'dy'}{[(x-x')^2+(y-y')^2+z^2]^{\frac{3}{2}}(x'^2+y'^2+\gamma^2)^{\frac{1}{2}}}$$

$$+\frac{p}{4\pi\varepsilon_0} \int_{x'=a}^{x'=b} \int_{y'=c}^{y'=d}$$

$$\times \frac{3z[x'(x-x')+y(y-y')-z\gamma]dx'dy'}{[(x-x')^2+(y-y')^2+z^2]^{\frac{5}{2}}(x'^2+y'^2+\gamma^2)^{\frac{1}{2}}} \cdot \quad (13)$$

The limits *a*, *b*, *c* and *d* are determined by the size of the sheet and the position of the point to which all the dipoles align:

$$b-a = S_1$$

$$d-c = S_2$$

where S_1 is the length of one side of the sheet and S_2 is the other side. (E. g., let the size of the sheet be 100 Å by 100 Å, $S_1 = S_2 = 100$ Å, and the point of alignment be below the bottom right hand corner of the sheet; then $a = -100$, $b = 0$, $c = 0$ and $d = 100$.)

2.2 *Field contours and isopotentials*

Utilizing eqs. (11)–(13) an IBM 7044 computer was programmed to determine the field under a square sheet of dipoles 180 Å × 180 Å at 30 fixed field points. The zero coordinate is taken at one corner of the square. For each fixed field point to which all the dipoles aligned, over 1000 field values were obtained in the domain. To represent these force field values beneath the square dipole array, two-dimensional plots were made of over 100 planes beneath the sheet. Utilizing two fixed field points as being representative of this analysis, $(0, 0, 10)$ and $(0, 0, 130)$, plots are reproduced here of the isopotentials or field contours cutting the following planes (see figs. 56–66):

Fig.	Plane	Fixed coordinate	Field component
56	x-y	$z = 10$ Å	E_x
57	x-y	$z = 70$ Å	E_x
58	x-y	$z = 130$ Å	E_x
59	x-y	$z = 10$ Å	E_z
60	x-y	$z = 70$ Å	E_z
61	x-y	$z = 130$ Å	E_z
62	z-x	$y = 90$ Å	E_z
63	z-x	$y = 170$ Å	E_z
64	z-x	$y = 210$ Å	E_z
65	z-x	$y = 90$ Å	E_x
66	z-x	$y = 130$ Å	E_x

(The E_y component is symmetric to the E_x component.)

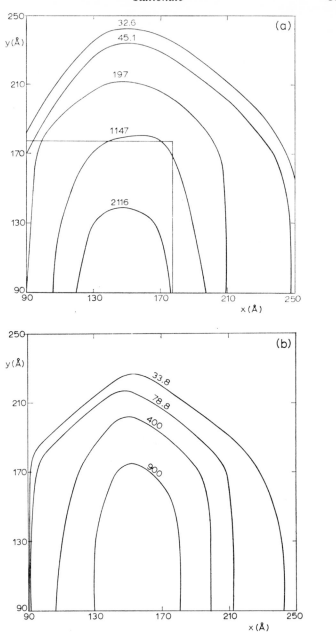

Fig. 56. E_x field ($\times 10^8$) in the $z = 10$ plane. (a) P.O.L. (0, 0, 10), (b) P.O.L. (0, 0, 130)

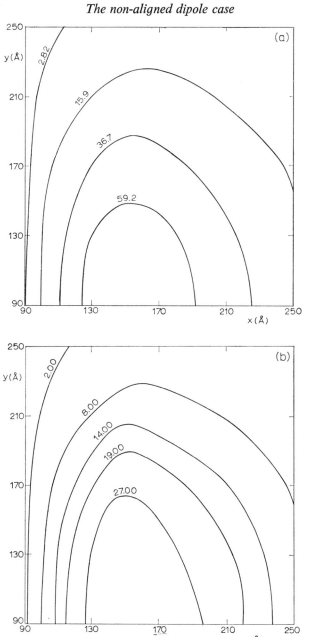

Fig. 57. E_x field ($\times 10^8$) in the $z = 70$ plane. (a) P.O.L. $(0, 0, 10)$, (b) $(0, 0, 130)$

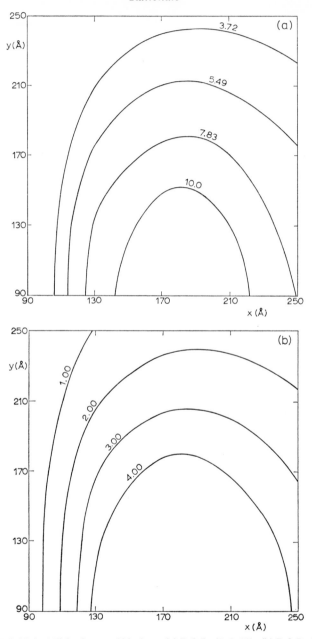

Fig. 58. E_x field ($\times 10^8$) in the $z = 130$ plane. (a) P.O.L. (0, 0, 10), (b) P.O.L. (0, 0, 130)

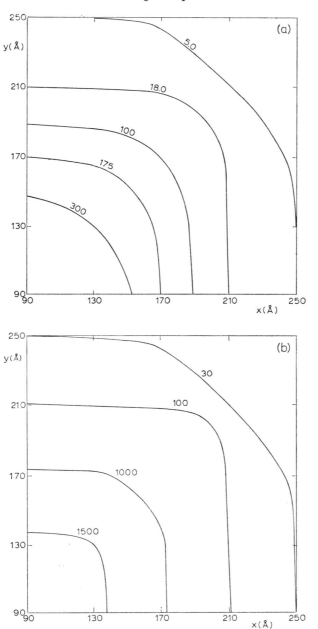

Fig. 59. E_z field ($\times 10^8$) in the $z = 10$ plane. (a) P.O.L. (0, 0, 10), (b) P.O.L. (0, 0, 130)

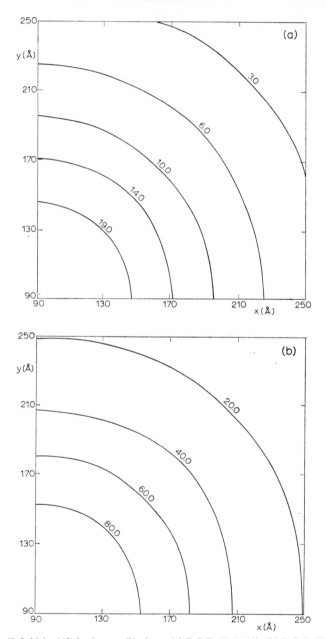

Fig. 60. E_z field ($\times 10^8$) in the $z = 70$ plane. (a) P.O.L. (0, 0, 10), (b) P.O.L. (0, 0, 130)

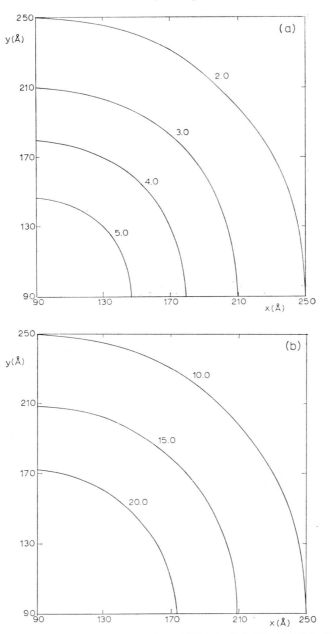

Fig. 61. E_z field ($\times 10^8$) in the $z = 130$ plane. (a) P.O.L. (0, 0, 10), (b) P.O.L. (0, 0, 130)

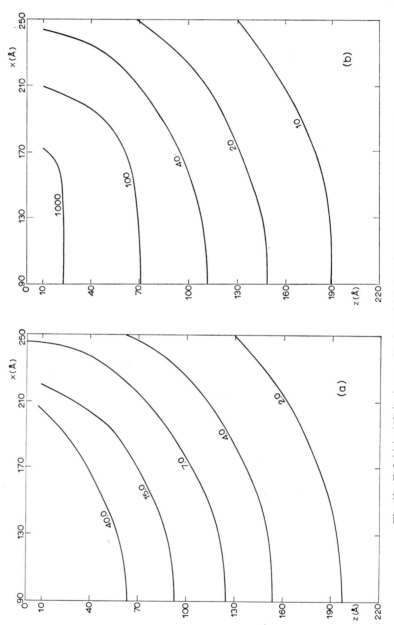

Fig. 62. E_z field ($\times 10^8$) in the $y = 90$ plane. (a) P.O.L. (0, 0, 10), (b) P.O.L. (0, 0, 130)

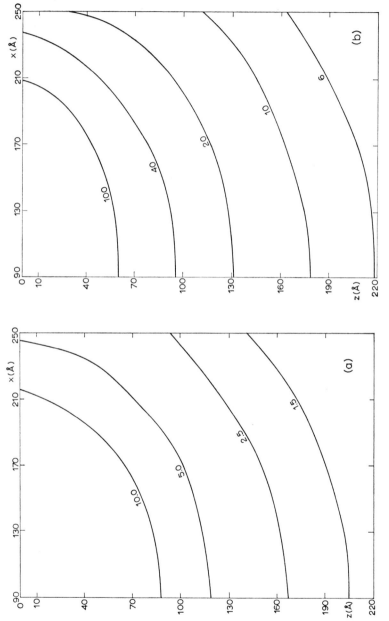

Fig. 63. E_z field ($\times 10^8$) in the $y = 170$ plane. (a) P.O.L. (0, 0, 10), (b) P.O.L. (0, 0, 130)

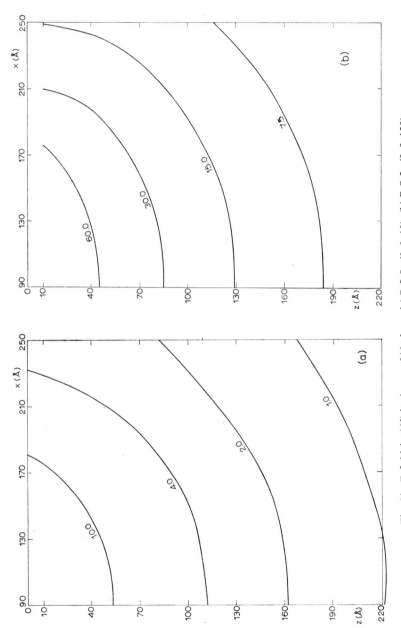

Fig. 64. E_z field ($\times 10^8$) in the $y = 210$ plane. (a) P.O.L. (0, 0, 10), (b) P.O.L. (0, 0, 130)

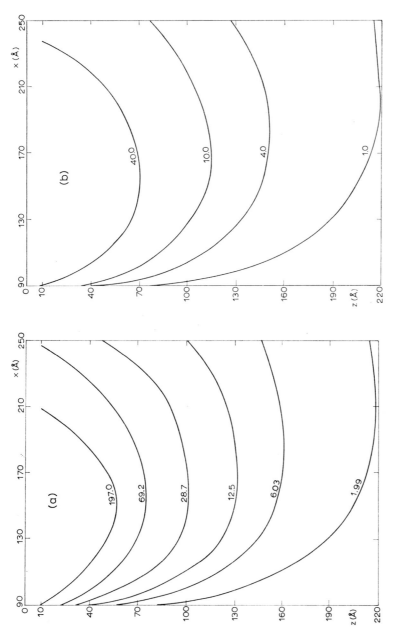

Fig. 65. E_x field ($\times 10^8$) in the $y = 90$ plane. (a) P.O.L. (0, 0, 10), (b) P.O.L. (0, 0, 130)

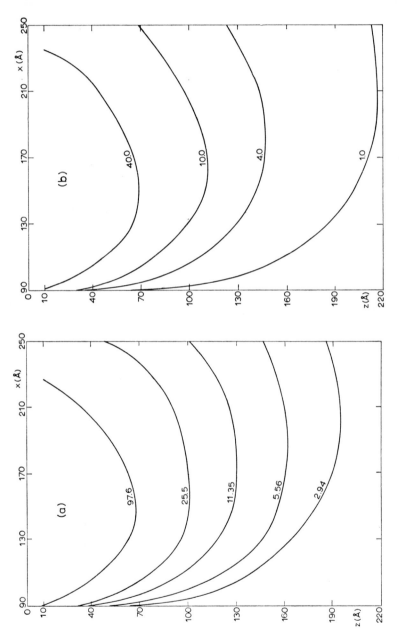

Fig. 66. E_x field ($\times 10^8$) in the $y = 130$ plane. (a) P.O.L. (0, 0, 10), (b) P.O.L. (0, 0, 130)

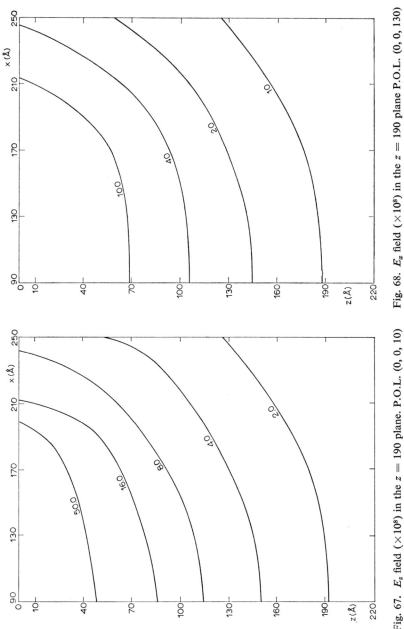

Fig. 68. E_x field ($\times 10^8$) in the $z = 190$ plane P.O.L. (0, 0, 130)

Fig. 67. E_z field ($\times 10^8$) in the $z = 190$ plane. P.O.L. (0, 0, 10)

Two additional graphs are included for the "point of alignment" (P.O.L.) (0, 0, 130) for E_z and E_x field contours of the *x-y* plane at $z =$ 190 for purposes of comparison (see figs. 67,68). Only one quarter of the dipole array and domain are shown in these graphs as the field has four-

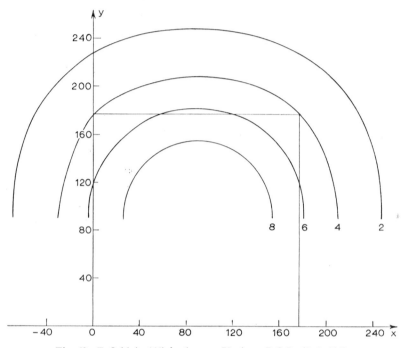

Fig. 69. E_z field ($\times 10^9$) in the $z = 70$ plane. P.O.L. (0, 0, 130)

fold symmetry. Two graphs are shown [P.O.L. (0, 0, 130), E_z components, *x-y* plane, $z = 70$, and *x-z* plane, $y = 90$] in addition to the above (see figs. 69, 70) to show the full dimensions of the dipole sheet and the extent of the field contours.

The following observations can be made in moving the P.O.L. from (0, 0, 10) to (0, 0, 130): the E_x and E_y components show the greatest change in field strength near a quadrant center (whose values of *x, y* and *z* are 150, 150, 0). A comparison of field strength with the two P.O.L. (0, 0, 10) and (0, 0, 130) at the quadrant center indicates that the former is approximately five times the latter. This maximum difference in magnitude drops to nearly zero for distances greater than twice the sheet length.

A comparison of E_z values indicates that with the two P.O.L. a constant ratio $(E_{z=130}/E_{z=10})$ of field values is observed. Thus, throughout the entire domain, the ratio of field values (a maximum in the system) of approximately five is maintained.

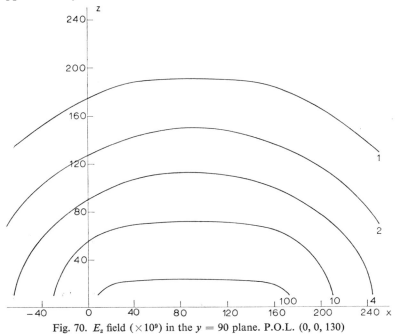

Fig. 70. E_z field ($\times 10^9$) in the $y = 90$ plane. P.O.L. (0, 0, 130)

These comparisons of field values (E_x, E_y, E_z) indicate only very small *differences* in forces. Thus, in utilizing the above *maximum ratios*, the difference in any field value is well under an order of magnitude.

2.3 *Line graphs*

In considering the two P.O.L. chosen above, (0, 0, 10) and (0, 0, 130), as representative of the domain the above isopotentials or field contours have been graphed to aid in visualizing a comparison of field values within the various planes. However, these contours do not show the functional dependence of the field components on the coordinates as clearly as a set of line graphs where only one coordinate varies at a time. To demonstrate this property of the system at the same two P.O.L., four sets of graphs, E_z vs z, E_x vs z, and E_x vs x, E_z vs x have been drawn at the following fixed coordinates (see figs. 71–77)

E_z vs z, E_x vs z	E_x vs x, E_z vs x
(90, 90, z)	(x, 90, 10)
(130, 90, z)	(x, 90, 70)
(170, 90, z)	(x, 130, 10)
(130, 130, z)	(x, 130, 70)
(170, 130, z)	(x, 170, 10)
(170, 170, z)	(x, 170, 170)

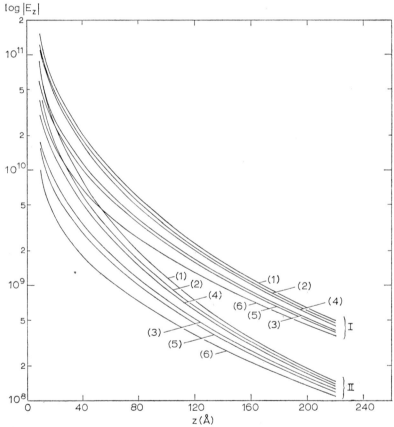

Fig. 71. E_z vs. z. Curves I: P.O.L. (88.6, 88.6, 130); curves II: P.O.L. (88.6, 88.6, 10). $E_z > 0$ for all cases, z represents the distance below the sheet. The parameters for the curves are the following coordinates (labels 1–6):

(1)	(90, 90, z)	(3)	(170, 90, z)	(5)	(170, 130, z)
(2)	(130, 90, z)	(4)	(130, 130, z)	(6)	(170, 170, z)

One may observe from these graphs that the field components depend primarily on their respective coordinate.

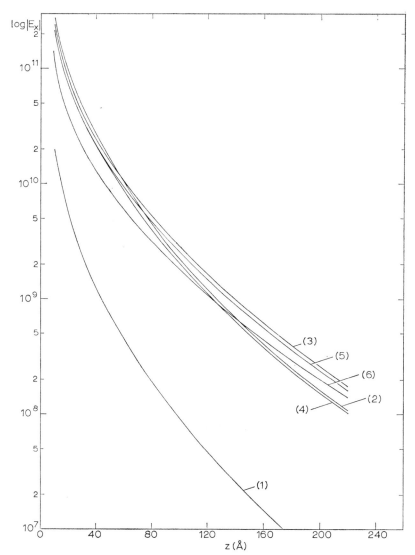

Fig. 72. E_x vs. z. P.O.L. (88.6, 88.6, 10). $E_x < 0$ for all cases. Labels 1–6 represent same parameters as in fig. 71

Thus, $E_z \approx E_z(z)$, $E_x \approx E_x(x)$ and $E_y \approx E_y(y)$. The change in the point of alignment from (0, 0, 10) to (0, 0, 130) causes only slight variation in the E_x component. However, the E_z component increases approx-

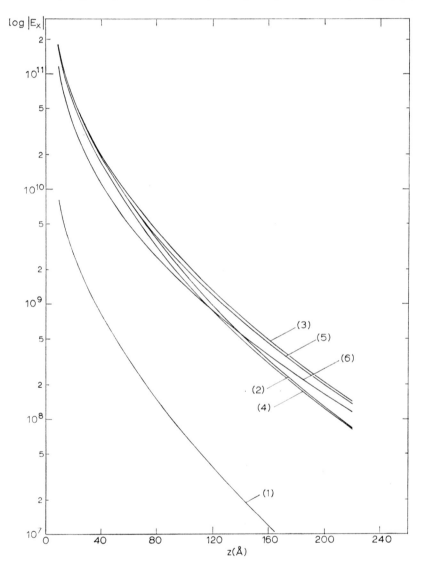

Fig. 73. As fig. 72. P.O.L. (88.6, 88.6, 130)

imately 5 times when the P.O.L. is moved from $z = 10$ to $z = 130$. (This was noted previously from the isopotentials or field contours.) These line graphs also show a rapid change in field strength in moving from $x = 170$ to $x = 210$ in the $z = 10$ plane. This spurious result may be explained by the proximity to the edge of the sheet.

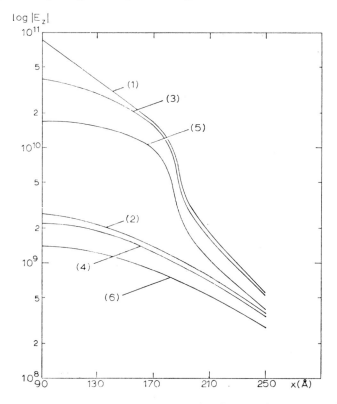

Fig. 74. E_z vs. x. P.O.L. (88.6, 88.6, 10). $E_z > 0$ for all cases. The parameters for the curves are the following coordinates (labels 1–6):

(1)	$(x, 90, 10)$	(3)	$(x, 130, 10)$	(5)	$(x, 170, 10)$
(2)	$(x, 90, 70)$	(4)	$(x, 130, 70)$	(6)	$(x, 170, 70)$

3 The flat quadrupole sheet. The bilayer structure

3.1 Linear arrays of point charges (derivation)

The purpose of this section is to derive a closed form solution for the field due to a rectangular sheet of linear quadrupoles. The approach will be to assume sheets of discrete charges which when added together in the limiting process, will form a single sheet of linear quadrupoles. The field equations for each charge sheet when superpositioned, will yield the field equation for the quadrupole sheet.

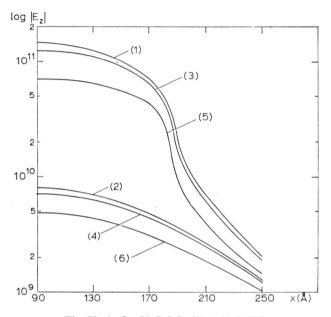

Fig. 75. As fig. 74. P.O.L. (88.6, 88.6, 130)

A quadrupole is specifically defined here to refer to two dipoles so oriented that their charges lie on a linear axis (see fig. 78). The quadrupole is further defined such that the individual dipole vectors will point in opposite directions along the line. A positive quadrupole will be one in which the dipole vectors point away from each other. For this derivation, the orientation line shall be perpendicular to the plane of quadrupoles and parallel to the z coordinate axis (see fig. 79). The linear distance between the dipole charges is a, and the distance between dipoles is $2b$. The origin of the coordinate system is taken at the field point P. The sheet (quadrupole) is given dimensions of $2w$ and $2L$ in the x and y directions respectively. The coordinates of the center of the sheet are (x_1, y_1, z_1).

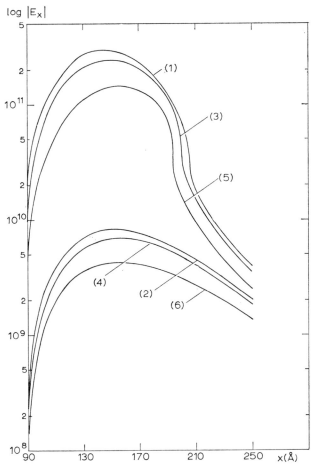

Fig. 76. E_x vs. x. P.O.L. (88.6, 88.6, 10). $E_x < 0$ for all cases. Labels 1–6 represent same parameters as in fig. 74

The distance vector to the center Q of a single quadrupole is denoted r (see fig. 79). The distance to each charge of the quadrupole is given by the vectors r_1, r_2, r_3 and r_4:

$$r_1^2 = (z+a+b)^2 + R^2$$
$$r_2^2 = (z+b)^2 + R^2$$
$$r_3^2 = (z-b)^2 + R^2$$
$$r_4^2 = (z-b-a)^2 + R^2$$

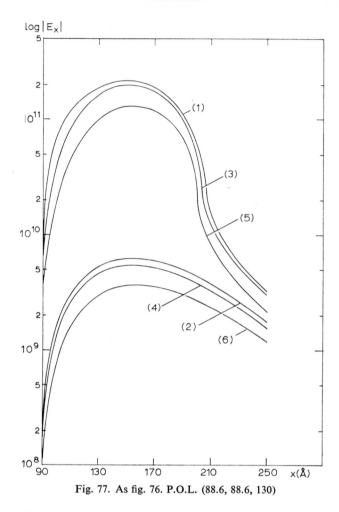

Fig. 77. As fig. 76. P.O.L. (88.6, 88.6, 130)

where $R^2 = x^2 + y^2$. The field and potential equations for each charge are defined as follows:

$$E = \frac{q\hat{a}_r}{4\pi\varepsilon_0 r^2} \tag{14}$$

where $\hat{a}_r \equiv$ unit vector in the r direction from P to Q, and

$$V_P = \int_\infty^r E \cdot dr. \tag{15}$$

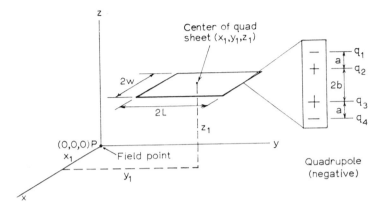

Fig. 78. Coordinate axes of quadrupole sheet

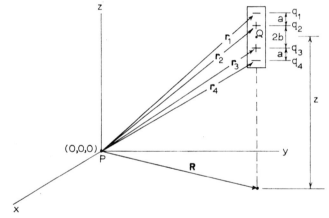

Fig. 79. Distance vectors for each charge of quadrupole

Substituting eq. (14) into eq. (15), integrating and taking into account the direction of the defined unit vector $\hat{a}_r$, yields:

$$V_P(q_n) = \frac{q_n}{4\pi\varepsilon_0 r_n} \tag{16}$$

where $n = 1, 2, 3$ or 4 and $V_P(q_n) \equiv$ potential at P due to each charge q_n. The total potential V_P at the field point $P(0, 0, 0)$ from a single quadrupole is equal to the sum of the individual potentials from each charge.

$$V_P = \sum_{n=1}^{4} V_P(q_n) = [V_P(q_1) + V_P(q_2) + V_P(q_3) + V_P(q_4)] . \tag{17}$$

In forming a whole sheet of quadrupoles, the potential at P can be determined by summing the potential due to each individual quadrupole.

Let $V_{Ps} \equiv$ potential at P due to the quadrupole sheet, i.e. the sum of the potentials due to each charge sheet. Then

$$V_{Ps} = \sum_{\delta=1}^{m} V_{Pj} \tag{18}$$

where m is the number of quadrupoles and V_{Pj} the potential due to the jth quadrupole. It follows that

$$V_{Pj} = \sum_{n=1}^{4} V_P(q_n)_j \tag{19}$$

and

$$V_{Ps} = \sum_{\delta=1}^{m} \sum_{n=1}^{4} V_P(q_n)_j . \tag{20}$$

By taking the limit as $m \to \infty$ and $|q_n| \to 0$, the following integral equation can be formed:

$$V_{Ps} = \int_A \sum_{n=1}^{4} \frac{\varrho V_P(q_n)}{|q_n|} dA, \tag{21}$$

where ϱ is the charge density (also the quadrupole density). Let

$$\varrho = \frac{1.602 \times 10^{-19} \text{ coulomb}}{(5 \times 10^{-10})^2 \text{ meter}^2} = 0.642 \text{ coulomb/m}^2. \tag{22}$$

The charge density is determined by the packing configuration of the individual dipoles. In this derivation, square packing is assumed and each charge has the magnitude of one electron.

Inserting the limits and differential area into eq. (21) the total potential equation may be represented by

$$V_{Ps} = -\frac{\varrho}{4\pi\varepsilon_0} \sum_{n=1}^{4} \int_{x=x_1-w}^{x_1+w} \int_{y=y_1-L}^{y_1+L} \left(-\frac{1}{r_1} + \frac{1}{r_2} + \frac{1}{r_3} + \frac{1}{r_4} \right) dx\,dy \tag{23}$$

or the more useful form

$$V_{\text{Ps}} = -\frac{\varrho}{4\pi\varepsilon_0} \sum_{n=1}^{4} \int_{x=x_1-w}^{x_1+w} \int_{y=y_1-L}^{y_1+L} \frac{\delta(n)\mathrm{d}x\,\mathrm{d}y}{(d_n^2+x^2+y^2)^{\frac{1}{2}}} \tag{24}$$

where

$$\delta(n) = \begin{cases} -1, & n = 1, 4 \\ +1, & n = 2, 3 \end{cases} \qquad d_n^2 = r_n^2 - x^2 - y^2;$$

e.g. $\delta(1) = -1$, $d_1^2 = (z+a+b)^2$. Integrating eq. (24) with respect to x yields

$$V_{\text{Ps}} = -\frac{\varrho}{4\pi\varepsilon_0} \sum_{n=1}^{4} \int_{y=y_1-L}^{y_1+L} \ln\left(\frac{(x_1+w)+[(x_1+w)^2+y^2+d_n^2]^{\frac{1}{2}}}{(x_1-w)+[(x_1-w)^2+y^2+d_n^2]^{\frac{1}{2}}}\right)\delta(n)\mathrm{d}y. \tag{25}$$

Integrating equation (24) with respect to y yields

$$V_{\text{Ps}} = -\frac{\varrho}{4\pi\varepsilon_0} \sum_{n=1}^{4} \int_{x=x_1-w}^{x_1+w} \ln\left(\frac{(y_1+L)+[x^2+(y_1+L)^2+d_n^2]^{\frac{1}{2}}}{(y_1-L)+[x^2+(y_1-L)^2+d_n^2]^{\frac{1}{2}}}\right)\delta(n)\mathrm{d}x. \tag{26}$$

Since the field is equal to the negative gradient of the potential, one of the integrations can be bypassed by utilizing Leibnitz's rule [2]):

$$\frac{\mathrm{d}}{\mathrm{d}t}\int_{a(t)}^{b(t)} f(x, t)\mathrm{d}x = f[b(t), t]b'(t) - f[a(t), t]a'(t) + \int_{a(t)}^{b(t)} \frac{\partial f}{\partial t}(x, t)\mathrm{d}x.$$

Thus, using the following transformations

$$x = x_1 \pm w, \qquad y = y_1 \pm L, \qquad z = z_1;$$

$$\mathrm{d}x = \mathrm{d}x_1, \qquad \mathrm{d}y = \mathrm{d}y_1, \qquad \mathrm{d}z = \mathrm{d}z_1; \tag{27}$$

$$\mathbf{E} = -\nabla V, \tag{28}$$

$$\nabla = \frac{\partial \hat{\imath}}{\partial x_1} + \frac{\partial \hat{\jmath}}{\partial y_1} + \frac{\partial \hat{k}}{\partial z_1}; \tag{29}$$

we have

$$E_x = -\partial V_{\text{Ps}}/\partial x_1 \tag{30}$$

$$E_y = -\partial V_{\text{Ps}}/\partial y_1 \tag{31}$$

$$E_z = -\partial V_{\text{Ps}}/\partial z_1. \tag{32}$$

Combining eqs. (30) and (26) gives an equation for the field in the x-direction:

$$E_x = \frac{\varrho}{4\pi\varepsilon_0} \left(\frac{\partial}{\partial x_1}\right) \sum_{n=1}^{4} \int_{x=x_1-w}^{x_1+w} \ln\left(\frac{(y_1+L)+[x^2+(y_1+L)^2+d_n^2]^{\frac{1}{2}}}{(y_1-L)+[x^2+(y_1-L)^2+d_n^2]^{\frac{1}{2}}}\right)\delta(n)\mathrm{d}x$$

(33)

which is in the form of Leibnitz's Rule. Performing the indicated operations and utilizing Leibnitz's Rule gives

$$E_x = \frac{\varrho}{4\pi\varepsilon_0} \sum_{n=1}^{4} \left(\ln\frac{(y_1+L)+[(x_1+w)^2+(y_1+L)^2+d_n^2]^{\frac{1}{2}}}{(y_1-L)+[(x_1+w)^2+(y_1-L)^2+d_n^2]^{\frac{1}{2}}}\right.$$

$$\left.-\ln\frac{(y_1+L)+[(x_1-w)^2+(y_1+L)^2+d_n^2]^{\frac{1}{2}}}{(y_1-L)+[(x_1-w)^2+(y_1-L)^2+d_n^2]^{\frac{1}{2}}}\right)\delta(n).$$

(34)

In a similar manner, combining eqs. (31) and (25) and performing the indicated operations utilizing Leibnitz's rule, yields

$$E_y = \frac{\varrho}{4\pi\varepsilon_0} \sum_{n=1}^{4} \left(\ln\frac{(x_1+w)+[(x_1+w)^2+(y_1-L)^2+d_n^2]^{\frac{1}{2}}}{(x_1-w)+[(x_1-w)^2+(y_1+L)^2+d_n^2]^{\frac{1}{2}}}\right.$$

$$\left.-\ln\frac{(x_1+w)+[(x_1+w)^2+(y_1-L)^2+d_n^2]^{\frac{1}{2}}}{(x_1-w)+[(x_1-w)^2+(y_1-L)^2+d_n^2]^{\frac{1}{2}}}\right)\delta(n).$$

(35)

Eqs. (34) and (35) represent the field in the x and y-directions from a quadrupole sheet.

Differentiating eq. (24) with respect to z leaves

$$E_z = \frac{\varrho}{4\pi\varepsilon_0} \sum_{n=1}^{4} \int_A \frac{-d_n}{(d_n^2+x^2+y^2)^{\frac{3}{2}}} \delta(n) \, \mathrm{d}A$$

(36)

where $\partial(d_n)/\partial z = 1$.

Integrating with respect to x yields

$$E_z = \frac{\varrho}{4\pi\varepsilon_0} \sum_{n=1}^{4} \int_y \frac{-d_n x}{(d_n^2+y^2)(x^2+y^2+d_n^2)^{\frac{1}{2}}} \Bigg|_{x=x_1-w}^{x_1+w} \delta(n) \, \mathrm{d}y.$$

(37)

Integrating over the y coordinate

$$E_z = -\frac{\varrho}{4\pi\varepsilon_0} \sum_{n=1}^{4} \tan^{-1}\left[\frac{xy}{d_n(x^2+y^2+d_n^2)^{\frac{1}{2}}}\right]\Bigg|_{x=x_1-w}^{x_1+w}\Bigg|_{y_1-L}^{y_1+L}\delta(n).$$

(38)

Expanding and substituting the integral limits yields the field in the
z-direction from a quadrupole sheet

$$E_z = -\frac{\varrho}{4\pi\varepsilon_0} \sum_{n=1}^{4} \left(\tan^{-1} \left[\frac{(x_1+w)(y_1+L)}{d_n[d_n^2+(x_1-w)^2+(y_1+L)^2]^{\frac{1}{2}}} \right] \right.$$

$$-\tan^{-1} \left[\frac{(x_1-w)(y_1+L)}{d_n[d_n^2+(x_1-w)^2+(y_1+L)^2]^{\frac{1}{2}}} \right]$$

$$-\tan^{-1} \left[\frac{(x_1+w)(y_1-L)}{d_n[d_n^2+(x_1+w)^2+(y_1-L)^2]^{\frac{1}{2}}} \right]$$

$$\left. +\tan^{-1} \left[\frac{(x_1-w)(y_1-L)}{d_n[d_n^2+(x_1-w)^2+(y_1-L)^2]^{\frac{1}{2}}} \right] \right) \delta(n). \qquad (39)$$

Eqs. (34) and (35) satisfy the following boundary conditions (by symmetry)

(a) When $x_1 = y_1 = 0$, $E_x = E_y = 0$.
(b) When $w = L = 0$, $E_x = E_y = 0$.
(c) For $x_1 = y_1 = L = w$, $E_x = E_y$.

Eq. (39) satisfies the following boundary conditions:

(a) When point P is in a plane which is coplanar with one of the charge
    sheets, the E_z field at P due to the charge sheet must be equal to zero.
(b) For $w = L = 0$, $E_z = 0$.

3.2 Calculations and discussion

It is useful to compare values for specific field points evaluated from
equations (34), (35) and (39) with the analogous field points of the dipole
aligned case (ch. 7). The following constants being representative of the
domain were substituted for two cases in the above equations.

Quadrupole sheet

Calculation of E_x	Calculation of E_z
$z = 100 \text{ Å}+a+b$	$z = 100 \text{ Å}+a+b$
$a = 3 \text{ Å}, b = 25 \text{ Å}$	$a = 3 \text{ Å}, b = 25 \text{ Å}$
$L = 90 \text{ Å}$	$L = 90 \text{ Å}$
$w = 90 \text{ Å}$	$w = 90 \text{ Å}$
$x_1 = y_1 = 90 \text{ Å}$	$x_1 = y_1 = 0$

$$E_{x1} + E_{x2} = -5.63 \times 10^7 \qquad E_{z1} + E_{z2} = -8.70 \times 10^7$$
$$E_{x3} + E_{x4} = 1.22 \times 10^8 \qquad E_{z3} + E_{z4} = 7.61 \times 10^8$$
$$E_x = 6.57 \times 10^7 \qquad E_z = 6.74 \times 10^8$$

Dipole aligned sheet

Calculation of E_x	Calculation of E_z
$z = 100$ Å	$z = 100$ Å
$x_1 = 90$ Å	$x_1 = y_1 = 0$
$y_1 = 0$ Å	
$E_x = 3.0 \times 10^9$	$E_z = 4.8 \times 10^9$

A comparison of the field values for the quadrupole sheet and the dipole aligned sheet indicates that for the E_z component the fields differ by approximately an order of magnitude. For the E_x component, the fields differ by two orders of magnitude. However, the single dipole layer $(E_{x3} + E_{x4})$ in the quadrupole derivation, where the dipoles are perpendicular to the sheet, differ from the aligned case by an order of magnitude. It is reasonable to assume from these studies, that if the quadrupole sheet were *aligned* for *maximum* effect to a field point (not perpendicular to the sheet as in the above derivation, for *minimum* effect) then the field difference would be no more than an order of magnitude. For the E_z component considering $E_{z3} + E_{z4}$, the field difference from the dipole aligned case is less than an order of magnitude. Thus, one may conclude from the above analysis that the second layer of dipoles in the bilayer structure influences the E_x and E_y components most and in general, reduces the field by an order of magnitude when compared to the dipole aligned case.

It is to be noted, that in the above derivation the only assumption, not based on experimental data, that may influence the calculations is that the quadrupole sheet is considered "continuous". The only restriction this imposes on eqs. (21), (22) and (26) is that the distance from the field point P to the quadrupole sheet must be at least the distance between individual quadrupoles which is 5 Å. Thus, this derivation is valid for any distance greater than 7 Å from the sheet.

It is also to be noted in this derivation that equations (34), (35) and (39) are highly sensitive to the values chosen for a and b. If a goes to zero the values for the field equations vanish. This is equivalent to superimposing and bringing together the positive and negative charges in a dipole. The value of *a* was selected as an average value somewhere between the separation of charge in the polar group of a lecithin and fatty acid molecule.

If *b* goes to zero, the field does not vanish but is greatly reduced. This is equivalent to placing the two dipole layers back to back. The value of *b* selected for this derivation (25 Å) is the closest approach possible for the two dipole layers. It is more likely that the two layers are somewhere between 25 and 100 Å apart. The further apart the two layers are placed, the less effect the second layer has in subtracting field from the first and the larger the field values from the quadrupole sheet become.

4 *Organization in biological cells*

4.1 *Methods*

The two derivations given in this chapter show that a model of membrane structure based on a single surface of aligned dipoles is a reasonable approximation of the field to the orientation events that could occur in the bilayer phospholipid biological case. It is only necessary now to consider closed surfaces to map the field effects within differently shaped biological cells. This work has been completed for (1) the sphere, (2) the parallelepiped and (3) the cylinder. The specific details of these cases with field contour maps are given in chapters 9–11. Here only the general methods and general character of the results will be discussed.

In chapter 4 the influence of geometry has been described on a dipole aligned surface of a circular flat sheet considering only the axis of symmetry. That analysis is useful only for a first approximation to determine the order of magnitude of the field in the domain. With a closed surface several new and important field effects originate from the superposition of fields. Thus the simplest approach is to consider six flat dipole sheets of various dimensions juxtapositioned to form a parallelepiped. By summing the fields in three directions in a computer program new field contour maps can be drawn for the enclosed domain. By varying the sizes of the sheets the effect on the field contours within the enclosed space may be studied.

Similar types of analysis have been used to describe the field contours within a sphere and a cylinder. The application of field effects for the cylindrical case to nerve physiology has stimulated further analyses for the cylinder of orientation effects of dipoles and the use of the bilayer model (a double dipole sheet).

4.2 *Characteristics of force fields*

Within a closed figure bounded by a surface of dipoles (free to orient themselves to every point in the domain) it has been found that the force fields vary in sign and magnitude in a systematic manner dependent upon the geometry of the closed surface and the location within the cell. A useful representation of these force fields is the zero isopotential field contours within these three-dimensional figures. Unlike the zero field values beneath a finite flat sheet of dipoles, where at some points the electric field intensity is actually equal to zero (no field), a zero field in a closed figure represents an equilibrium event where the high field values from all sides superimposed are equal and oppositely directed. Thus the *net* field is zero at such points where charged molecules would be held in equilibrium unable to move.

The zero contour has several other characteristics useful in describing the force fields within these three-dimensional closed figures. The zero isopotential usually divides the cell into geometrical compartments which alternate in sign as one crosses the zero field boundary. The shape of these compartments are a function of the geometry of the closed surface and may be studied by varying the dimensions of the cell. Since the force field closely adjacent to the surface of the cell is at its maximum, the size of compartment given by the zero contour line shows the rate of change in field values. Also, in this way, the location of high and low field values within a compartment may be easily defined. In addition the field contours within the compartments will have similar shapes to the zero field lines.

By comparing the zero contours, for example with the cube, the variation in lengthening four of its sides forming a parallelepiped 2, 10 or 100 times its length, shows marked changes occurring in the shape and location of compartments. It is hoped that these changes will be useful in understanding the physiological functions that differently shaped cells perform.

With the cylinder, dynamic analyses have been considered showing the movement of charged entities as a function of their location within the cell. The influence of the orientation of the dipoles has also been studied.

5 *Summary*

The rationale for the use of a "dipole aligned model" to represent the biological membrane is set forth in detail. The basis for selecting this model system over and against other fixed charge, dipole and quadrupole configurations, is implemented with two derivations of (1) a quadrupole sheet and (2) field functions adjacent to an aligned dipole sheet (the field is determined other than at the point of alignment). The general characteristics and properties of closed geometric figures (sphere, cube, parallelepiped and cylinder) simulating model biological cells, utilizing this membrane representation, are described. The significance of these force fields in the organization and ordering processes within biological cells is considered.

6 *References*

[1] Stoeckenius, W., Symp. Internatl. Soc. Cell Biol. **1** (Academic Press, N. Y., 1963) p. 349.
[2] Kaplan, W., *Advanced Calculus* (Addison-Wesley Publ. Co., Reading, Mass., 1959) p. 220.

Chapter 9

The sphere

Contents

1 *Introduction*

In considering closed geometrical figures, the sphere is often chosen for analyses because of the simplicity in dealing with its high degree of symmetry. For the biological membrane model described in chapters 1–8 where the electric field and potential functions are of paramount interest, this point of view is *not* sustained. Rather, the high symmetry of a spherical surface of charges or dipoles sometimes hides the true field effects due to this surface model. The cancellation of force fields within

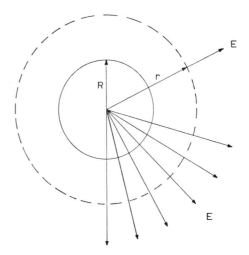

Fig. 80. A uniform conducting sphere of surface charge

the sphere often yields a zero resultant field vector. However, this may be interpreted to mean that the sum of the fields at a given point are equal and oppositely directed. Thus some of the analyses give no insight into the magnitude of this equilibrium force. Yet these values may be quite high at a given point despite the fact that the E vector is zero. For this reason, which will be amplified further in this chapter, the sphere is a difficult choice for describing field effects. It is the general purpose here to summarize what useful information *has* been obtained on the application of this membrane model to the sphere since it is the most common geometric form.

Classical electrostatic treatments of a sphere of charges are well known. These analyses are concerned with a uniform *conducting* sphere of surface charges and do not apply to uniform *fixed* charges, dipoles or quadrupoles as in this membrane model. However, it is of interest to review the field and potential equations for a *conducting* sphere, to allow a comparison with the *fixed* charge and dipole model.

In considering a uniform, conducting sphere of surface charge (σ) (see fig. 80), the integral equation for vacuum conditions is given by

$$\varepsilon_0 \int\int \boldsymbol{E} \cdot \boldsymbol{r}\mathrm{d}a = Q \tag{1}$$

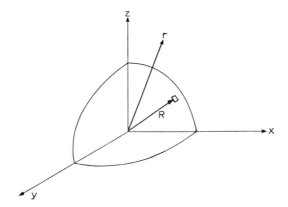

Fig. 81. A sphere of homogeneous fixed surface charge

where

ε_0 = permittivity of free space

$\boldsymbol{E}$ = electric field intensity vector

$\boldsymbol{r}$ = distance vector from the center of the sphere (origin) to the field point

$\mathrm{d}a$ = differential of area

Q = unit charge

Utilizing Gauss's law, it may easily be shown that

$$\varepsilon_0 E(4\pi r^2) = \sigma(4\pi R^2) \tag{2}$$

and

$$E = \frac{\sigma}{\varepsilon_0} \left(\frac{R}{r} \right)^2 \tag{3}$$

a well known relation for a conducting sphere. When $r < R$, the special case for inside the sphere, it may further be shown that $E = 0$ and that inside the sphere is at an equipotential.

The immediate question is whether for a homogeneous, uniform, *fixed* charge distribution the same equations hold. Starting with the potential function (see fig. 81)

$$\Phi = \frac{1}{4\pi\varepsilon_0} \int_0^\pi \int_0^{2\pi} \frac{\sigma \, da}{r} = \frac{\sigma R^2}{4\pi\varepsilon_0} \int_0^\pi \int_0^{2\pi} \frac{\sin\theta \, d\varphi \, d\theta}{r} \tag{4}$$

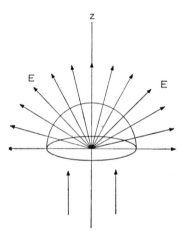

Fig. 82. A hemisphere of fixed surface charge

yields

$$\Phi = \frac{\sigma R^2}{\varepsilon_0 r}. \tag{5}$$

If $r < R$

$$\Phi = \frac{\sigma R^2}{\varepsilon_0 R} = \frac{\sigma}{\varepsilon_0} R. \tag{6}$$

In the general case

$$E = -\nabla\Phi = -\frac{d}{dr}\Phi = -\frac{d}{dr}\left(\frac{\sigma R^2}{\varepsilon_0} \right) \frac{1}{r} = \frac{\sigma R^2}{\varepsilon_0 r^2}. \tag{7}$$

When $r < R$ (inside the sphere) differentiating eq. (6) with respect to r gives

$$E = 0 \qquad\qquad (8)$$

as with the conducting sphere.

In a similar manner, one may consider the field from a fixed charged hemisphere in the hope of ascertaining some measure of the magnitude of the force field *inside* the domain. This is equally unrewarding (see fig. 82), the field is zero within the hemisphere and approximately zero below the hemisphere.

It is assumed that other investigators have treated the above case and on the basis of these unrewarding results, have discarded any form of a charge or dipole model for a closed surface. It will be shown in the next section that the dipole model *does* yield field values of significance within the sphere when all the dipoles are assumed to align to the field point. Thus some information can be gained of the field values within the sphere useful for comparison to other geometrical closed surfaces.

2 *Derivation*: *spherical dipole surface*

Together with the dipole aligned model for the biological membrane of chapters 1–8, the following definitions are utilized in this derivation (see fig. 83):

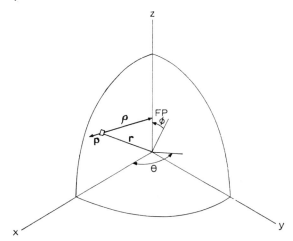

Fig. 83. A sphere of fixed aligned dipoles

P = dipole moment per unit area

$P \cdot \varrho = -|P||\varrho|$

FP = field point located a distance z on the z-axis

R = radius of the sphere.

The potential function is given by

$$\Phi = \frac{1}{4\pi\varepsilon_0} \iint_{\text{sphere}} \frac{P \cdot \varrho \, da}{|\varrho|^3}. \tag{9}$$

Substituting for the differential area and ϱ, where

$$|\varrho|^2 = R^2 + z^2 - 2zR \cos \varphi,$$

yields

$$\Phi = \frac{-|P|R^2}{4\pi\varepsilon_0} \int_0^{2\pi} \int_0^\pi \frac{\sin \varphi \, d\varphi \, d\theta}{R^2 + z^2 - 2zR \cos \varphi}. \tag{10}$$

Evaluating the definite integrals gives

$$\Phi = \frac{-|P|R}{4\varepsilon_0 z} \left[\ln \left(R^2 + z^2 + 2zR \right) - \ln \left(R^2 + z^2 - 2zR \right) \right]. \tag{11}$$

Rearranging yields

$$\Phi = \frac{-|P|R}{2\varepsilon_0 z} \ln \left(\frac{R+z}{R-z} \right). \tag{12}$$

Since

$$E_z = -\nabla\Phi = \frac{-\partial\Phi}{\partial z}, \tag{13}$$

by differentiating eq. (12) with respect to z

$$E_z = \frac{|P|R}{2z\varepsilon_0} \left[\frac{1}{R+z} + \frac{1}{R-z} \right] - \left[\frac{|P|R}{2\varepsilon_0} \frac{1}{z^2} \left(\ln \frac{R+z}{R-z} \right) \right]. \tag{14}$$

Rearranging yields

$$E_z = \frac{-|P|R}{2z\varepsilon_0} \left[\frac{-2R}{(R^2 - z^2)} + \frac{1}{z} \ln \left(\frac{R+z}{R-z} \right) \right]. \tag{15}$$

Recalling that z represents the distance from the center of the sphere to the field point and R represents the radius of the sphere, eq. (15) represents the electrostatic field of aligned dipoles as a function of radial position only. Eq. (15) satisfies the boundary conditions

$$E_z = 0 \text{ at } z = 0, \qquad E_z > 0 \text{ for } 0 > z < R$$

$$E_z = 0 \text{ at } z \to \infty$$

$$\text{For } R \leqq z < \infty, \lim_{z \to R} E_z = \infty. \tag{16}$$

3 *Calculations and discussion*

Equation (15) has been programmed for an IBM 7044 computer for four values of R (10^3 Å, 5×10^3 Å, 10^4 Å and 5×10^4 Å) utilizing the value of p given in chapters 1–8. Plots of $\log(z/R)$ vs $\log E_z$ are given in fig. 84. It is apparent from this comparison of graphs that for a given ratio of z/R, the smaller the sphere the more intense the field. Thus P.P.L.O.'s (pleura pneumonia like organisms) which have been characterized as small as 400 Å in diameter (smallest known organisms) may well develop fields of 10^8 to 10^{11} newton/coulomb *within* the cell.

Considering values of $z/R < 0.5$ the curves of fig. 84 are of the form

$$\log E_z = \log A + B \log (z/R) \tag{17}$$

where $B = 1$. Rearranging

$$A = E_z/(z/R). \tag{18}$$

Picking a specific ratio, let $z/R = 0.1$. Then

$$R_1 = 10^3 \qquad E_z = 1.28 \times 10^8$$
$$R_2 = 5 \times 10^3 \qquad E_z = 2.56 \times 10^7$$
$$R_3 = 10^4 \qquad E_z = 1.28 \times 10^7$$
$$R_4 = 5 \times 10^4 \qquad E_z = 2.56 \times 10^6$$

or $E_z = 1.28 \times 10^{11}(1/R)$ at $z/R = 0.1$. Therefore, utilizing these values in eq. (18) $A = 1.28 \times 10^{12}(1/R)$. Substituting this value for A in the general equation (17) yields

$$E_z = 1.28 \times 10^{12}(z/R^2) \qquad \text{for} \qquad (z/R) < 0.5$$

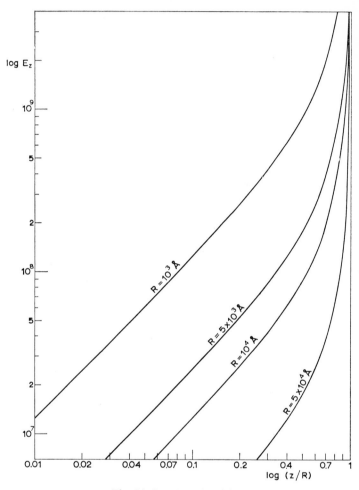

Fig. 84. Log E_z vs log (z/R)

where z and R are in *angströms*, or

$$E_z = 1.28 \times 10^{22}(z/R^2) \qquad \text{for} \quad z/R < 0.5 \tag{19}$$

where z and R are in *meters*, which gives the field in newton/coulomb.

Eq. (19) gives a simple and rapid approximation of the field within a sphere when $z/R < 0.5$ assuming this dipole membrane model.

4 *Summary*

The difficulties inherent in applying a charged membrane model, to determine the electric field intensity within a sphere, is explained. It is shown that the field equations for a *conducting* charged sphere are identical to those for a *fixed* charged sphere and are of little help in evaluating the magnitude of the field within the domain. However, a derivation utilizing a *dipole aligned surface membrane model* does allow evaluation of the field effects as a function of radial position. While varying the radius of the sphere for four cases, plots of $\log E_z$ vs $\log (z/R)$ are evaluated and discussed. From these graphs, a further simplified expression for determining the field within a sphere is obtained.

Chapter 10

Parallelepipeds

Contents

1 *Introduction*

In chapters 1–5 emphasis has been given to electrostatic field effects beneath a flat, rectangular and circular array of homogeneous dipoles. The model system for the biological membrane has been developed by considering alternative arrangements of fixed charge, dipole, and quadrupole sheets (see chapter 8). It has been shown that a single *dipole aligned sheet* is an excellent approximation to the more structurally accurate quadrupole case (representing the bimolecular lipid leaflet), and accurately represents the field for a fixed charge and a dipole non-aligned case. Thus by allowing the dipoles of a sheet to realign to each new field point within the domain, an excellent measure is obtained of the force fields originating in the skeleton structure of all biological membranes. In chapter 9, this dipole aligned model has been applied to a sphere, with a surface of oriented dipoles, but the technical difficulties in treating this highly symmetric closed figure have yielded only limited results. This is due to the fact that the force field contours within the sphere (originating within the surface) are spherical in shape and analyses add only knowledge of the field magnitudes within the domain.

This is not the case with the parallelepiped. By forming six flat rectangular *dipole aligned sheets* into a closed figure with all right angles, the summation of force fields within the figure show significant organizational properties within the domain. By varying the dimensions of the sheets, the character of these organizational properties within the parallelepiped may be studied.

The derivation of field equations for the *dipole aligned flat rectangular sheet* is given in chapter 5. An IBM 7044 has been programmed to superposition the six flat dipole aligned sheets for four cases:

Case 1. The cube ($10^4 \times 10^4 \times 10^4$ Å)
Case 2. Elongated ($10^4 \times 10^4 \times 2 \times 10^4$ Å)
Case 3. Elongated ($10^4 \times 10^4 \times 10^5$ Å)
Case 4. Elongated ($10^3 \times 10^3 \times 10^5$ Å).

These cases were chosen so as to be representative of the biological dimensions of cells and useful in studying the change in field contours within the parallelepiped as it is elongated.

Three methods have been chosen to represent these force fields within these three-dimensional figures. First, three-dimensional contour maps have been accurately graphed for cases 1 and 2 and a transition state from case 1 to case 2 for the zero field contour. From these figures, to be described in detail, one is able to evaluate the organizational properties of the cells based on these force fields rapidly and accurately. Second,

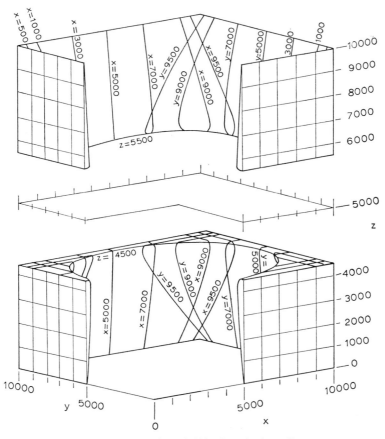

Fig. 85. Zero force field in the cube (case 1)

two-dimensional graphs of isopotentials or field contours have been accurately plotted for cases 1, 2 and 3 for two representative planes. These graphs show clearly the changes in the organizational properties of the cell as the parallelepiped is elongated. Third, one-dimensional line

graphs are used for the latter three cases to show the functional dependence of the fields on the specific walls of the parallelepiped.

For the three-dimensional and two-dimensional graphs, only the zero
contours are shown. Most can be learned by studying these graphs since
other force field contours will have analogous shapes. The magnitudes

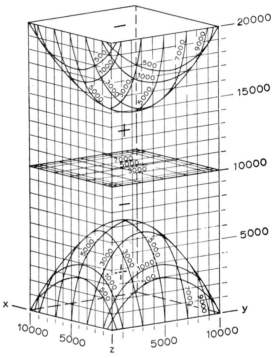

Fig. 86. Zero force field (axonometric projection) of $2 \times 1 \times 1$ parallelepiped (case 2)

of the force fields within the four cases studied may be gleaned from the
line graphs.

The biological significance of these analyses is discussed in section 4.
No attempt has been made to detail these applications. Emphasis has
been given to ways of representing these findings rather than elaborating
the many relationships to biological problems. This emphasis is based
on the idea that *ordering* and *selective processes* within biological cells
are a function of the non-statistical approach of this model system and
the elucidation of this basic mechanism is of prime importance.

2 *Organization in cell contents*

2.1 *Zero contours*

In figs. 85–87 are represented in that order (1) a cut-away in three dimensions of a plot of part of the zero force field contour in the cube (case 1);

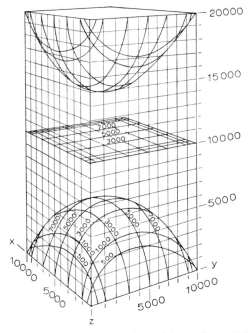

Fig. 87. Zero force field (perspective plot) of $2 \times 1 \times 1$ parallelepiped (case 2)

(2) an *axonometric projection* of the E_z zero force field contour of the $2 \times 1 \times 1$ parallelepiped (case 2); (3) a *perspective plot* of the E_z zero force field of the $2 \times 1 \times 1$ parallelepiped (case 2). Fig. 85 describes part of the E_x, E_y zero force field contours along the sides and an E_z zero plane bisecting the cube in half. The E_x and E_y zero mid-planes bisecting the cube in the other two directions are not shown. The E_z zero contours for the top and bottom planes are also omitted for clarity. In figs. 86 and 87 the E_x and E_y zero contours are similarly omitted for the sake of clarity.

In order to follow the "growth" of the zero force field contours from

the cube through the elongated parallelepipeds two *x,z*-planes (at
$y = 500$ Å and $y = 5000$ Å) have been chosen to represent these iso-

Figs. 88, 89, 90. *x-z* planes at $y = 500$ Å
for cases 1, 2, and 3

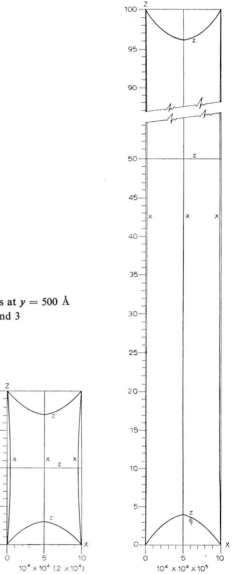

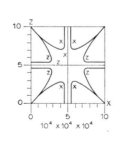

potential surfaces in cases 1, 2 and 3. These are shown in figs. 88 through 93. All graphs have been plotted from computer data and drawn to scale.

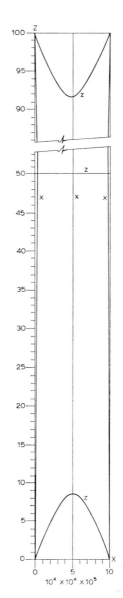

Figs. 91, 92, 93. *x-z* planes at *y* = 5 000 Å
for cases 1, 2 and 3

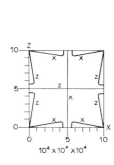

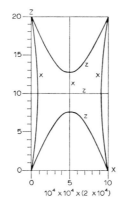

Cases 3 and 4 for the E_z zero contours may be visualized by graphs similar to case 2 as shown in figs. 86 and 87, where the parallelepiped has been extended. The zero force field contours may be pictured by considering figures 89, 90, 92 and 93. However, the transition from the cube to the $2 \times 1 \times 1$ parallelepiped is not as simple a change. It will be

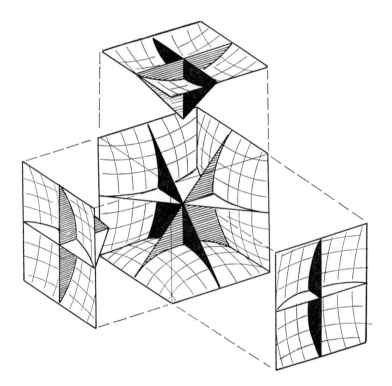

Fig. 94. Transition state from the cube to elongated parallelepiped

noted from figs. 88 and 91 that the zero planes bisecting the cube are perpendicular to their respective zero E component contours along the sides (thus, the E_x zero contour bisecting the cube is at right angles to the E_x contours along the sides). This is in contrast to the elongated cases where the E_z mid zero field plane bisects the parallelepiped in the same direction as the E_z zero contours along the top and bottom. It follows that the cube must go through a transition state in the process of elongating. This transition state is pictured in figure 94 as an artist's conception of how the cube must look at some point before elongating to case 2.

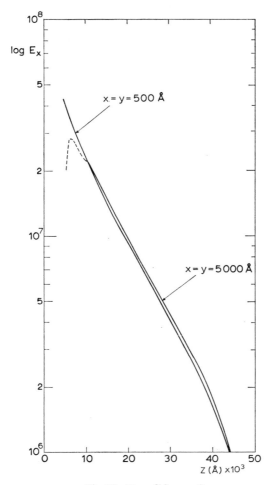

Fig. 95. $E_z = f(z)$, case 3

2.2 *Non-zero fields*

By inspection of figs. 85, 88 and 91 for case 1, it may be observed that a field component will be most affected by the sides of the cube which are perpendicular to it. The sides parallel to the field component will produce a small effect for distances greater than one twentieth (1/20) of the cube length.

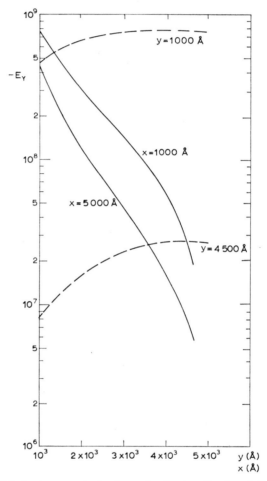

Fig. 96. $E_y = f(x)$, for two constant values of y (broken lines) and $E_y = f(y)$, for two constant values of x (full lines)

In figs. 85, 86 and 87, the zero field contours may be used to evaluate the magnitudes of the fields on either side of the zero surface. The field on the surface is zero. Moving away from the zero surface towards the walls the field builds up rapidly to the order of magnitude of 10^8 newton/coulomb within 500 Å away from the zero surface. The field strength stays at this order of magnitude to within 500 Å of the parallelepiped

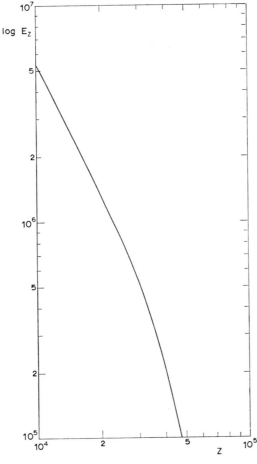

Fig. 97. $E_z = f(z)$, case 4

walls (or ends). At the walls the field rises rapidly. The directions of the field are given by the signs in the compartments formed by the zero contours. The central zero planes bisect the figures. Thus, for the $2 \times 1 \times 1$ parallelepiped, case 2, the zero planes (not all shown) are:

$$E_z = 0 \quad \text{for} \quad z = 10000 \text{ Å}$$

$$E_y = 0 \quad \text{for} \quad y = 5000 \text{ Å}$$

$$E_x = 0 \quad \text{for} \quad x = 5000 \text{ Å}.$$

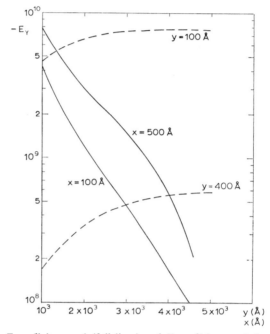

Fig. 98. $E_y = f(y)$, case 4 (full lines) and $E_y = f(x)$, case 4 (broken lines)

In case 3 the E_z variations as a function of z are shown in fig. 95. This graph indicates almost complete independence of E_z with respect to x and y for z *greater* than one tenth (1/10) the parallelepiped length. For z *less* than one tenth (1/10) the parallelepiped length the ends start to take effect. In fig. 95, the E_z field values will lie between the lines shown for $500 \leqq x, y \leqq 9500$ Å. Thus fig. 95 shows the variation of E_z as x and y are varied with z.

In fig. 96 the variation of E_y (of case 3) is plotted as a function of x for two constant values of y. The same field component E_y plotted as a function of y for two constant values of x is also given in that figure. All intermediate values of E_y will lie between the values of the four curves shown for the intermediate values of the x and y constants. In addition, the computer data indicate that the E_y field (in case 3) is not an appreciable function of z, variation occurring in the third significant digit within a given order of magnitude.

In case 4, the previous analyses hold with the following exceptions: E_z is now completely independent of x and y and E_y is completely independent of z. These observations are illustrated in figs. 97 and 98.

3 *Conclusions*

The most striking feature of the parallelepiped surface model is the organization of the cell into distinct compartments. Viewing case 2, the $2 \times 1 \times 1$ parallelepiped (being representative) as shown in figs. 86 and 87, one observes for the E_z component there are two half bubbles and a plane bisecting the figure. These zero field contours divide the domain into four regions whose E_z components are oppositely directed in each two adjacent regions. Thus a dipole or charged surface for a parallelepiped has the effect of *polarizing* the domain within the cell and organizing it into distinct compartments. The E_x and E_y components similarly compartmentalize the field in the x and y directions as shown in figs. 88 through 93. However, the half bubbles in the cube coalesce into very narrow bands along the sides for the elongated parallelepiped. The transition state as pictured in fig. 94 shows the complexity of these compartments in all three directions as one moves from the cube to the elongated case.

4 *Biological applications*

It is not possible to consider all the potential uses of these findings for biological cells. As in all theoretical studies, experimental verification is a prerequisite for proving their validity. That new techniques and methods *must* be developed, to detect differences in huge field values within the biological cell at the microscopic level, is apparent. Yet from a theoretical point of view, these results are conclusive and should be applied.

The results described in this chapter are most aptly related to three areas in biology: (1) structural organization of cells, (2) cell growth, and (3) nerve conduction.

The organization of the cell into compartments is well suited for studies of *mapping* biological structures of a cell. That the nucleus lies often at a midcentral point yields insight into the kinds of charged structures that must be present. A comparison of the charge configurations of macro-molecules within the nucleus as compared to the cytoplasm is a study long overdue. Cytologists and histologists can now develop a tool by which they can predict the probable location of a given macromolecule depending upon its charge configuration. Thus a study of the electro-static properties of charged macromolecules of differing arrangements will be the first step in this direction. In addition the mapping of organelles, endoplasma reticulum and other cellular structures may yield insight into the kinds of force fields involved in their physiological functioning.

The growth of cells may be considered by analyzing the rearrangement of force fields of the cube to form the $2 \times 1 \times 1$ elongated parallelepiped. An electrodynamic analysis of these events may yield a mechanism for mitotic division and explain the large forces required to separate the component parts of the nucleus.

For the $100 \times 1 \times 1$ parallelepiped, the E_x and E_y zero contours along the sides (well within 500 Å from the side) make it an ideal model for studying nerve conduction. The huge force fields that must exist between the wall and the zero contour may well lead to a mechanism by which sodium and potassium ions are pumped in and out of the cell.

5 *Summary*

An attempt has been made to apply the "dipole aligned surface model" of a biological membrane to a cube and elongated parallelepipeds, in an effort to study the organization and ordering properties of biological cells. By representing the zero and non-zero fields within the domain by three-dimensional contour maps, insight is gained into the mechanisms of (1) the structural organization of cells, (2) cell growth and (3) nerve conduction.

Chapter 11

The cylinder

Contents

1 *Introduction*

This chapter is devoted to electrostatic and electrodynamic properties of a dipole membrane model as applied to a cylinder. The purpose here is to present a mechanism by which a charged particle (or ion) may be conducted through an open cylinder whose walls are made up of dipoles oriented radially to the surface. At this stage, no attempt is being made to correlate these findings with biological events. However, derivations have been completed for (1) a closed cylinder of dipoles, (2) a closed cylinder of quadrupoles and (3) an analysis of orientation effects of dipoles for a closed cylinder, which show the relevance to the biological case of nerve conduction. These latter derivations will be published separately. Here the basic equations governing the electric field intensity along the axis of symmetry of a cylinder, composed of dipoles radially oriented to the surface, will be derived.

2 *Derivation*

The general equations for the electric field intensity and potential energy for a point dipole function (for a single dipole) will be derived such that the equations are immediately integrable over a cylindrical surface. In the general equations, the point dipole function is a *moment* function while in the cylindrical equations, the dipole function becomes a *moment density* function. Thus

$$\mathrm{d}\boldsymbol{P} = \frac{|\boldsymbol{P}|}{A_\mathrm{p}}\,\mathrm{d}A = \boldsymbol{p}\,\mathrm{d}A \qquad (1)$$

where

$\boldsymbol{P}$ = dipole moment
A_p = average area for single dipole
$\mathrm{d}\boldsymbol{P}$ = differential dipole element on a differential surface $\mathrm{d}A$
$\boldsymbol{p}$ = dipole density function.

The dipole density function $\boldsymbol{p}$ will have radial and z-directional components. The tangential component will not be considered. This derivation applies only to the axis of symmetry of the cylinder.

The potential of a point dipole is given by

$$V = \frac{1}{4\pi\varepsilon_0} \frac{\boldsymbol{P} \cdot \boldsymbol{\varrho}}{|\boldsymbol{\varrho}|^3}. \tag{2}$$

From fig. 99 the following vector equations obtain:

$$\boldsymbol{P} = \boldsymbol{P}_R + \boldsymbol{P}_z = |\boldsymbol{P}|(\sin\theta\,\hat{a}_R + \cos\theta\,\hat{a}_z) \tag{3}$$

$$\boldsymbol{\varrho} = R\hat{a}_R + R\cot\alpha\,\hat{a}_z \tag{4}$$

$$\boldsymbol{P} \cdot \boldsymbol{\varrho} = |\boldsymbol{P}|R\sin\theta + |\boldsymbol{P}|R\cos\theta\cot\alpha \tag{5}$$

$$|\boldsymbol{\varrho}| = (R^2 + R^2\cot^2\alpha)^{\frac{1}{2}} = R\,\mathrm{cosec}\,\alpha \tag{6}$$

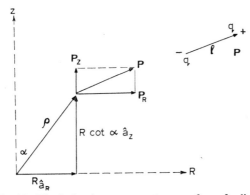

Fig. 99. Dipole density components on surface of cylinder

where $\hat{a}_R$ and $\hat{a}_z$ are unit vectors in the R and z directions respectively. Substituting eqs. (5) and (6) into eq. (2) and simplifying, yields

$$V = \frac{|\boldsymbol{p}|}{4\pi\varepsilon_0\,R^2}\left[\sin^2\alpha\cos(\alpha-\theta)\right]. \tag{7}$$

To determine the field, $\boldsymbol{E} = -\nabla V$, where

$$\nabla = \frac{\partial}{\partial R}\,\hat{a}_R + \frac{1}{R}\frac{\partial}{\partial\varphi}\,\hat{a}_\varphi + \frac{\partial}{\partial z}\,\hat{a}_z. \tag{8}$$

The field in the φ-direction is perpendicular to the z and R-axes (according to the right hand rule, $z \times R = \varphi$) and is given by

$$E_\varphi = -\frac{1}{R}\frac{\partial V}{\partial \varphi} = 0. \tag{9}$$

Utilizing eqs. (7) and (8) again, the field in the R-direction is given by

$$E_R = -\frac{|p|}{2\pi\varepsilon_0\,R^3}\,[\sin^2\alpha\,\cos(\alpha-\theta)]. \tag{10}$$

To evaluate the E_z field, one observes from fig. 99 that

$$z = R\cot\alpha \tag{11}$$

and

$$\frac{\partial z}{\partial \alpha} = -R\,\mathrm{cosec}^2\alpha \tag{12}$$

or

$$\frac{\partial \alpha}{\partial z} = -\frac{\sin^2\alpha}{R}. \tag{13}$$

Applying the chain rule to the gradient in the z-direction gives

$$\frac{\partial V}{\partial z} = \frac{\partial V}{\partial \alpha}\frac{\partial \alpha}{\partial z}. \tag{14}$$

Incorporating eq. (14) into eq. (8) yields

$$E_z = -\frac{\partial V}{\partial z} = -\frac{\partial V}{\partial \alpha}\frac{\partial \alpha}{\partial z} = \frac{\sin^2\alpha}{R}\frac{\partial V}{\partial \alpha}. \tag{15}$$

Substituting eq. (7) into eq. (15) and simplifying gives the final result

$$E_z = \frac{|P|}{4\pi\varepsilon_0}\frac{\sin^2\alpha}{R^3}\,[3\sin\theta\,\sin^2\alpha\,\cos\alpha+\cos\theta\,\sin\alpha(3\cos^2\alpha-1)]. \tag{16}$$

Eqs. (9), (10) and (16) represent the field at a point due to a single dipole on the cylinder. It is the purpose now to sum up the fields from a cylindrical configuration of dipoles.

An element of field may be defined dE whose origin is an elemental dipole dP

$$\mathrm{d}E = \frac{E}{P}\,\mathrm{d}P \tag{17}$$

where E is the total field of eqs. (9), (10) and (16). Thus dE will be the element of field at point (P) a distance and direction ϱ from the elemental dipole (see fig. 100). In order to determine the total field at point P from all the elemental dipoles on the cylinder

$$E_{\text{total}} = \int_s dE = \int_s \frac{E}{P} dP \tag{18}$$

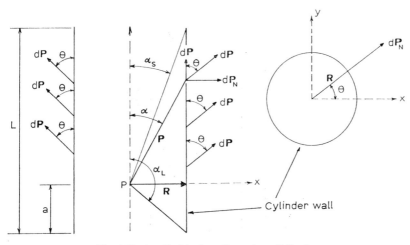

Fig. 100. A cylindrical configuration of dipoles

recalling that

$$dP = pdA \tag{1}$$

and the differential area element of a cylinder is given by

$$dA = r d\varphi dz. \tag{19}$$

In order to establish the limits of integration the following substitution is made

$$dz = \frac{\partial z}{\partial \alpha} d\alpha + \frac{\partial z}{\partial r} dr.$$

As $dr = 0$,

$$dz = \frac{\partial z}{\partial \alpha} d\alpha. \tag{20}$$

But from eq. (12)

$$\frac{\partial z}{\partial \alpha} = -\frac{R}{\sin^2 \alpha} \, .$$ (12)

Thus

$$\mathrm{d}z = \frac{-R}{\sin^2 \alpha} \, \mathrm{d}\alpha.$$ (21)

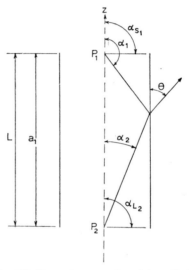

Fig. 101. Dynamic properties of the cylinder

The limits of integration in terms of α are α_s and α_L where α_s is the smallest angle of orientation to the z-axis and α_L is the largest angle of orientation to the z-axis. Thus from fig. 101

$$\alpha_s = \alpha_{\min} = \cot^{-1}[(L-a)/R],$$
$$\alpha_L = \alpha_{\max} = \cot^{-1}[-a/R];$$ (22)

φ may be integrated 360° around the cylinder.

Considering first the radial component substitute eq. (10) into eq. (17) yielding

$$\mathrm{d}E_R = \frac{E}{p} \, \mathrm{d}P = \frac{-\sin^2 \alpha \cos (\alpha - \theta)}{2\pi\varepsilon_0 R^3} \, pR \, \mathrm{d}\varphi \, \mathrm{d}z.$$ (23)

Thus from eq. (18) and (23)

$$E_R = \int_{\varphi=0}^{\pi} dE_R + \int_{\varphi=0}^{-\pi} dE_R = 0. \tag{24}$$

Considering the differential z-field from eq. (17) and (16)

$$dE_z = \frac{E_z}{p} dp = p \left[\frac{3 \sin \theta \sin^2\alpha + \cos \theta \sin \alpha (3 \cos^2\alpha - 1)}{4\pi\varepsilon_0 R} \right] d\varphi \, d\alpha. \tag{25}$$

Therefore

$$E_z = 4 \int_{\varphi=0}^{\pi/2} \int_{\alpha} dE_z = 2\pi p \int_{\alpha=\alpha_s}^{\alpha_L}$$

$$\times \frac{3 \sin \theta \sin^2\alpha \cos \alpha + \cos \theta \sin \alpha (3 \cos^2\alpha - 1)}{4\pi\varepsilon_0 R} \, d\alpha. \tag{26}$$

Performing the integration with respect to α gives the E_z field on the axis of symmetry of a cylindrical configuration of dipoles at a point (see fig. 101) which is a distance a above the edge of the cylinder of length L:

$$E_z = \frac{|p|}{2\varepsilon_0 R} [\sin^2\alpha_L \cos(\alpha_L - \theta) - \sin^2\alpha_s \cos(\alpha_s - \theta)]. \tag{27}$$

Summarizing the information from this derivation for the cylinder

$$E_\varphi = E_R = 0$$
$$E_z = \text{eq. (27)}$$
$$|p| = \text{dipole moment density}$$
$$\alpha_L = \alpha_{\text{max.}} = \cot^{-1}[-a/R]$$
$$\alpha_s = \alpha_{\text{min.}} = \cot^{-1}[(L-a)/R] \tag{22}$$
$$L = \text{cylinder length}$$
$$a = \text{distance above the edge of the cylinder}$$
$$R = \text{cylinder radius.}$$

Verification of equations (9), (24) and (27) may be obtained by an alternate approach in which the differential potential function is integrated over the entire surface giving the total potential function for the cylinder. By taking the gradient of this potential function, equations identical to the above are found.

Considering the special cases of eq. (27) where the dipoles of the cylinder (a) all align to the field point ($\alpha = 0$), (b) the dipoles are all perpendicular to the cylinder ($\theta = 90°$) and (c) the dipoles are tangent to the cylinder ($\theta = 0$), it is seen that:

for aligned dipoles ($\alpha = 0$)

$$E_z = \frac{|\mathbf{p}|}{2\varepsilon_0 R}(\sin^2\alpha_L - \sin^2\alpha_s);$$ (28)

for perpendicular dipoles ($\theta = 90°$)

$$E_z = \frac{|\mathbf{p}|}{2\varepsilon_0 R}(\sin^3\alpha_L - \sin^3\alpha_s);$$ (29)

for tangent dipoles ($\theta = 0$)

$$E_z = \frac{|\mathbf{p}|}{2\varepsilon_0 R}(\sin^2\alpha_L \cos\alpha_L - \sin^2\alpha_s \cos\alpha_s).$$ (30)

3 *Dynamic properties of the system*

A simple analysis of the dynamic properties of this system will give some measure of the events that may occur within a cylindrical membrane structure. Starting with a definition of a force field from Newton's second law and charge dynamics,

$$\mathbf{F} = m\mathbf{a} \quad \text{and} \quad \mathbf{F} = Q\mathbf{E}$$ (31)

yields

$$\mathbf{a} = \frac{Q}{m}\mathbf{E}$$ (32)

where

> $\mathbf{a}$ = acceleration vector
> Q = a charge on the axis of symmetry
> m = mass of particle
> E_z = field from the cylinder.

Eq. (32) represents the acceleration of a particle (on the axis of symmetry) of charge to mass ratio Q/m within the electric field E_z generated by the surface. Consider fig. 101 and eq. (27) with definite limits

$$a_z = \frac{Q}{m} \frac{|p|}{2\varepsilon_0 R} \sin^2\alpha \cos(\alpha - \theta)|_{\alpha_s}^{\alpha_L} \tag{33}$$

where a_z is the acceleration along the axis of symmetry. Observing (from fig. 101) points at the two ends of the cylinder such that $\alpha_{s_1} = 90°$, $\alpha_{L_1} \approx 180°$ and $\alpha_{s_2} \approx 180°$ and $\alpha_{L_2} = 90°$, at P_1 and P_2

$$a_1 = \frac{Q}{m}|p| \sin\theta \tag{34}$$

$$a_2 = |p| \sin\theta. \tag{35}$$

Thus, a positive charge will always be accelerated toward the center of the cylinder for the aligned or perpendicular orientation of dipoles. For these cases ($\alpha = \theta$, and $\theta = 90°$) a maximum acceleration of $(Q/m)|p|$ exists. When the dipoles are in a tangent position ($\theta = 0$) the acceleration vanishes.

It is now possible to consider different orientations of dipoles. By equating eq. (33) to zero, it can be shown that at given points along the axis, the acceleration will be zero if α_s and α_L are independent of θ and if θ has a given orientation. Thus, if $\alpha_s = 30°$ and $\alpha_L = 120°$, which fixes point P on the axis, then the acceleration will be zero when all the dipoles have an orientation $\theta = 48.5°$. Similarly when $\alpha_s = 60°$ and $\alpha_L = 150°$, then the acceleration at P will be zero when $\theta = 131.5°$. A more detailed analysis of the variation of θ and α will be given in a later publication. It is the purpose here to indicate that with fixed α_s and α_L and a given fixed θ it is possible to establish a zero point anywhere along the axis.

It is of interest to consider the motion of a charged particle at one end of the cylinder. If the dipoles align to the charge ($\theta = \alpha$) or are perpendicular to the cylinder ($\theta = 90°$), the particle will accelerate until it reaches the center where it will then start to decelerate. If the orientation of θ is some other fixed angle, then the acceleration will depend upon where the zero point is located. Assume the zero point is located at the extreme end of the cylinder. Then the particle will continue to accelerate until it moves through the entire cylinder and passes the zero point. In this case, the particle will break loose from the field of the cylinder and act as if it were shot from a gun. If a chain of such cylinders were insulated (so that their fields did not interfere) they would act as excellent conductors of charged particles.

4 *Discussion*

It is not to be inferred from the above analyses that the acceleration of a charged particle through a cylinder whose surface is made up of dipoles is synonymous with nerve conduction. However, it has been shown in chapter 10 that in an elongated parallelepiped the E_z component *off* the axis of symmetry is very similar to the *on*-axis field. In a forthcoming publication, it will be shown that the E_z component on the axis of a *closed* cylinder is identical to the E_z component on the axis of an elongated parallelepiped. Although the above *open* cylinder derivation treats only the axis of symmetry, it establishes a mechanism by which charges can be transferred down the cylinder. By ultimately relating the E_z field to ion fluxes near the surface, it is possible to correlate these events into a mechanism of nerve conduction.

5 *Summary*

An electrostatic dipole model for biological membranes is applied to the surface of an open cylinder to determine the electric field intensity and potential energy functions along the axis of symmetry. A closed form solution is derived for the field equations by a novel approach in the use of vectors. A dynamic analysis of a charged particle on the axis of symmetry is described. The usefulness of these analyses in determining the role of membrane structure in nerve conduction is set forth.

Chapter 12

The nature of bound water
in biological membranes

Contents

1 *Introduction*

1.1 *General*

Experimental evidence of the structural basis of biological membranes at the molecular level must still be fragmentary until such time that chemical and physical methods are more refined, capable of analyzing the complex lipo-protein configurations known to exist. At best, these analyses will yield insight into the identity and molecular groupings in the lipo-protein bilayer now thought to prevail in all membrane configurations. Yet when this is known, it will be more difficult to assess the experimental means to determine the structures and functioning of *water molecules* which must play a vital role in and around these biological surfaces.

The purpose of *theoretical analyses* in the history of science has often been one of bridging the gap between known physical events and those areas in which experiments are either too difficult or impossible to perform. It is the purpose here to show that based on the most fundamental knowledge of membrane structure, electrostatic theory will yield much insight into the properties of water molecules associated with membranes.

The need for understanding both the chemical and physical aspects of water in and around membraneous structures is well substantiated in recent literature. Of paramount importance to many areas of the life sciences are those studies in cryobiology which are concerned with reversible and irreversible structural changes in the bonding of water in cellular components associated with temperature variations [1]). These studies emphasize the formation of ice crystals and free acid and base accompanying phase changes in crystalline and liquid water as major factors in the freezing and thawing of cells. Experiments with colloids have shown that a large percentage of water fails to freeze with decreasing temperature [2]). By a rapid freezing technique, Jones and Gurtner have found that the "bound water" (0.7 to 4.67 g of water per g of gelatin at $-30\,°C$) remains unfrozen. In similar experiments 55 % of water is unfrozen in dry siliceous gel at $-10\,°C$. Small droplets of water can be supercooled down to $-72\,°C$ without refreezing. Lewis and Tuttle have found that none of the water in the leaves of the round-leaved wintergreen (Pyrola rotundifolia) freezes in winter until a temperature of 0.032 °C is reached. Many more examples have been published [3-6]). Spores are the hardiest living cells and can retain their vitality after immersion in liquid helium (-271.15 °C) which is only a couple of degrees above absolute zero and exposure to vacuum. The creation of such terms as "bound water" and "ice-like structures" associated with membrane components, have been useful in considering these phenomena. However, these terms lack the accuracy and clarity of definition necessary for rigorous mathematical analyses. It is one purpose here to define such terms critically.

Permeability and transport phenomena across membranes have been another major area where the role of water molecules has either been ignored or relegated to macroscopic concepts of dielectric. Such ideas as "screening effects" and "solvation effects" of ions and macromolecules have often been invoked in a very qualitative sense. Vague reference to field effects of water dipoles relative to ion transport must be clarified in the light of electrostatic calculations based on specific knowledge already obtained of membrane conformation. Although the electrostatics and electrodynamics of *ions* in membrane structures based on the essential constituents of cellular surfaces will be treated at a later time, the evidence gathered here detailing the conditions and parameters useful in treating water molecules will clarify many of the problems associated with ion fluxes.

Recent investigations of the mechanisms of synthesis of protein via RNA and DNA have shown that incomplete knowledge of these processes is often tied in to the lack of understanding of the nature of the water associated with macromolecules. The experimental difficulties inherent in determining the electrostatics of water involved in macromolecular complexes reside in techniques for measuring field and potential differences at the microscopic level. Such measurements are within the range of technological "know how" presently available. However, current methods employ only macroscopic potential readings. The most sensitive detectors in use yield measurements over 100 Å, an area far too large to be useful for molecular field and potential values.

Before describing in detail current approaches to the study of water molecules associated with membranes, the essential facts concerning water in biological systems and membrane structure must be reviewed.

Estimates of water concentration in living cells range from 70–90 %. However, these values include all forms of water and it is important here to distinguish meaningfully water *bound* in someway directly with membrane structures and *free* water not intimately in contact with any part of the cell surface. This delineation of water associated with membrane systems may be relegated to 30–50 % of total membrane mass; a large value in considering any membrane configuration. Although membrane systems vary widely in extent in different kinds of cells [7]) (e.g. even within the same species: *Hyphomicrobium* and *Nitrosomonas europaea*), the plasma membrane, organelle membranes and the endoplasma reticulum encompass approximately 80–90 % of the mass of the cell.

Studies from surface chemistry and electronmicrographs of biological membranes [8]) indicate that the basic skeletal structure of cellular surfaces involves a "bimolecular lipid leaflet" approximately 40–100 Å thick in which the lipid molecules are arranged perpendicular to the plane of the membrane with their polar groups (dipoles oriented) outward. Although little is known of the adjacent protein structures, the lipid phase has been well characterized by synthetic experiments of artificial lipid membranes suggested first by Rudin and Mueller [10]) and more recently confirmed by other investigations [9,10]). Assuming only the simplest dipole (polar) configurations [11–14]) for the lipid bilayer, which has been thoroughly substantiated in experiment, it is possible to determine from electrostatic considerations the mechanisms of "bound water" adjacent to and in these surface structures.

1.2 *Current approaches to the water problem*

Information derived from theoretical studies of the nature of water "bounded" by a biological surface, has come primarily from three avenues of approach: (1) chemical, (2) geometric and (3) statistical. There is considerable overlap in these studies since many investigations have utilized all three points of view. However, it is helpful here to distinguish among these points of view in order to help clarify assumptions, methodology and applicability upon which these systems are based.

The chemical approach most often invoked regards chemical entities in terms of hydrates or adsorbed water. The most carefully derived studies in characterizing solvation or hydration phenomena involve X-ray diffraction of simple ions in solution. Although far removed from biological membrane systems, these and other studies [11]) produce rigorous evaluations of hydrated ions in solution. Thus, similar concepts of hydration phenomena have been carried over to the fixed polar lipid moieties immersed in aqueous membrane systems. In addition to the simple hydrates or adsorbed water phenomena aqueous complexes have been proposed, based on water structures incorporated into molecular chelates [12]). Other forms of loose bonding associated with water structures have also been characterized. The voluminous literature describing the ubiquitous hydrogen bond bridging peptide and lipid polar groups is one example. Clathrate or cage structures involving "trapped" water are less frequently described [13]).

There are a number of points in common between the *chemical* and *geometric* approach. Studies concerned with "fit" and "stereorelations" among components of membrane surfaces and water molecules must often take into account the bond angles assumed in chemical binding and the structural configuration of water dependent upon its physical state. Thus, studies attempting to employ a geometric pattern to the structural units of the membrane often incorporate the water molecules in a similar pattern taking into account the necessary bonding angles. Of great interest has been the work of Hechter and Warner [14,15]), who attempt to incorporate a hexagonal and pentagonal sheet structure to protein and water arrays between the bilayer and adjacent to the membrane. A specific geometric conformation for the protein coats of the surface is first assumed, in this type of analysis. Based on this chemical structure, water molecules "fit" into the surrounding "holes". Only in a limited number of ways can the water molecules be arranged within such a structure. The difficulties inherent in such a method depend upon the validity of protein structure assumed. Although the probabilities are great that linear rather than helical arrays of protein will be found, the number of linear conformations possible far exceed the few cases so far theoretically studied. Thus, at best, this is a dubious assumption as a basis for further structural studies associated with water.

Those biophysical analyses cognizant of the *high field values* in and adjacent to the membrane structure often refer to the "ice-like structures" of water which *must* be present under those conditions. Such "ice-like structures" refer to the tetrahedral bonding and hydrogen bonding found in solid ice rather than trigonal liquid water structures free of hydrogen bonding. Although "ice" itself (physical solid state) is not assumed to be present, the electrostatic field is thought to fix the water molecules in a rigid, hydrogen bonded array not necessarily tetrahedral.

A number of statistical approaches to the study of liquid water, to ascertain the geometrical relations possible within the liquid state, have recently been investigated. It is not the purpose here to review the many statistical theories involved with liquid water [16-19]) but rather to show relevance to the biological case. Of special note are the "significant structure" theory of Eyring [16]), and the "flickering cluster" theory of Scheraga [17]), both of whom have been equally concerned with water in biological systems [18, 19]). These theories begin their analyses with the usual Boltzmann expressions for a random array of molecules or dipoles. Eyring's theory evolves on the basis of the now classical partition function for a three-dimensional rigid rotator which embodies two microscopic structures of liquid water as a function of the macroscopic variables, temperature and volume. Scheraga's analyses proceed on the basis of partitioning of available energies among discrete levels based on the size of the hydrogen bonded water clusters formed. It is of interest to note that although extrapolations to the microscopic level to determine struc- tures are possible by both these methods, the actual configurations do not exist and these fictions are only useful as a device to manipulate macro- scopic variables. Thus the utility of these structural statistical theories at the microscopic level are limited.

Barlow and MacDonald [20]) realizing the difficulties inherent in treating the water dipoles as statistical entities, have utilized a modified double layer theory approach in which "discreteness of charge effects" is taken into account within the statistical theory. However, this modification assists only in correcting the macroscopic parameters since the correction still utilizes an "improved" dielectric constant. At the microscopic level, in considering real structures of water molecules, a dielectric constant has no physical meaning. Thus statistical methods have been of little assistance in creating a theory applicable to structures of individual water molecules at the microscopic level in the liquid state.

Turning to water associated with membraneous structures, statistical theory has been equally unrewarding. Applications of Scheraga's theory to protein components yield relatively little insight into what is actually occurring at the molecular level [21]). Statistical theory of adsorption isotherms of protein monolayers on water yields equally unrewarding findings relative to water structures [22]). Studies by Pethica [23]) and others [24]) who have developed such concepts as the depth of immersion of polar end groups of lipid molecules in a monolayer on water, fail in their attempts at describing *discrete* molecular events. Statistical methods by definition involve *continuous phenomena* at the *microscopic level* for arriving at correct macroscopic values. Thus statistical theory is not meant to describe discrete individual molecular events.

2 Non-uniform fields based on the electrostatics of membrane structure

Based on potential measurements of biological surfaces utilizing intra-cellular or extracellular (standard) references, 50 to 200 mV potential differences between electrodes have been observed. However, these methods of potential measurement of relatively large areas of surface are unable to detect potential differences as a function of distance to the membrane. Because of this fact, biophysicists have inferred that large field values exist within the "bilayer structure". They have been previously considered *uniform* in intensity. An evaluation by a non-statistical approach of the field of the lipid layers of the membrane shows the latter assumption not only to be incorrect but further leads to erroneous con-clusions on the nature of water molecules within this field. Thus on the basis of previous calculations of discrete membrane structure, it has been shown that high field values exist and the electric field intensity generated by the lipid polar groups is a function of the distance to the membrane. Therefore, any calculations involving water dipoles must take into account the effect of this *non-uniform* field.

In terms of the structure of the polar groups of the phospholipid in the bilayer, it may easily be shown that each surface generates a non-uniform field which goes to zero midway between the two sheets (see fig. 102).

3 Ice-like structures

References in the literature to "ice-like structures" often refer to the qualitative definition of water molecules in terms of tetrahedral bonding and *fixed* nature of these dipoles in a large *uniform field*.

Water molecules between the bilayer and on either side of it, must be analyzed from slightly different points of view. As described earlier in this chapter, the superpositioning of the non-uniform fields from the two phospholipid surfaces 40–100 Å apart (as shown in fig. 103), causes the

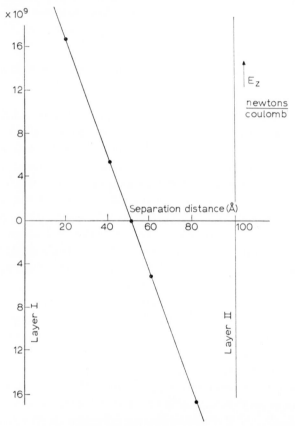

Fig. 102. Graph of the non-uniform field midway between the bilayer

field to go to zero at a mid-plane between them. The field on either side of the membrane does not go to zero except at an infinite distance away. This means that the field at any distance away from the membrane will always be finite and not equal to zero. The importance and usefulness of this concept will become apparent as this theory unfolds.

For locations on either side of a lipid surface (between the bilayer or adjacent to it), the water dipoles will first align in the field generated by that surface. Between the bilayer at the midcentral plane, the water dipoles

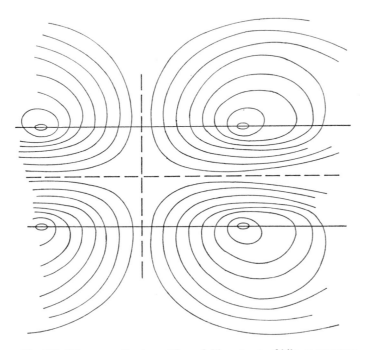

Fig. 103. Diagrammatic view of force field contours of bilayer structure

will be stationary. At all other points between the bilayer or adjacent to it, the dipoles will align themselves along the electric field lines which are radiating out from the two surfaces. This alignment process is based on the simple principle from electrostatics

$$\boldsymbol{p} \times \boldsymbol{E} = \boldsymbol{M} \qquad (1)$$

where $\boldsymbol{p}$ is the dipole moment of the water molecule in any given direction, $\boldsymbol{E}$ is the electric field generated by the surface and $\boldsymbol{M}$ is the torque acting on each individual dipole which aligns it in the field. When the dipoles are aligned $\boldsymbol{p} \times \boldsymbol{E} = 0$.

The electric field is non-uniform. This means that any dipole which is aligned in this field will translate in the direction of the field lines. Thus the water dipoles will first line up along the field lines and then will move towards the dipole surfaces. As they pack against the membrane surface, "ice-like structures" will be formed.

To expand this concept, the net translational force on a dipole which has aligned itself along a field line is

$$F_{trans} = p\nabla|E| \tag{2}$$

where F is the translational force acting on the dipole and p and E are defined as above.

Eq. (2) states that there is a net force no matter how small the gradient. Therefore, the ability to align along a field line is the dominant criterion for the formation of "ice-like structures".

This ability to form "ice-like structures" is dependent on the relative magnitudes of two effects. They are (a) the electric field and (b) the random thermal energy of the dipole. When the energy density in the electric field becomes less than the mean thermal energy of the water molecule, the dipole will tend *not* to line up. Mathematically stated, if

$$\tfrac{1}{2}\varepsilon_0 E^2 < \tfrac{3}{2}kT \tag{3}$$

the water dipoles will tend not to align. Thus, eqs. (1), (2) and (3) govern the formation of "ice-like structures".

Since the water dipoles move toward the walls (phospholipid surfaces) and collect on all sides, it is possible to define "ice-like structures" as those water structures (dipoles) formed at the walls which when "perturbed" will "relax" back to an equilibrium position. This equilibrium phenomenon, established solely on the electrostatics of the system, does not describe in any way the chemically bonded structures involved. However, it does place limitations on the packing and forces involved, based on equations (1)–(3).

The length of the water chains adjacent to the membrane structure will be limited by the force on each dipole due to the gradient of the field. When this force is of the order of magnitude of the random collision forces (mV_{av}/T_{coll}) where m = mass of molecule, V_{av} = average velocity and T_{coll} = collision time of the water dipole, it is unlikely that the molecule will move towards the surface. Thus the limiting factor in the length of the chains of water structures will be the distance from the surface where the random forces are greater than field effects.

4 *Bound water and protein structures*

Studies by Szent-Gyorgyi [25]) and Klotz [26]) have emphasized the importance of bound water as it relates to proteins in the cell. There is an extensive literature on this problem of bound water and proteins and several excellent reviews on the subject [27]). It is the purpose here to show how the theory postulated in this manuscript of "ice-like structures" fits into these points of view.

Denaturation of proteins has been linked with the "melting of ice" or the liberation of the "bound", "structured" or "organized" water which surrounds native protein molecules [28]). As previously described, it has been postulated that as much as 87 % of the water within the cell be bound or organized in some manner [29]). Bernal and Fowler [30]) suggested that the temperature at which water takes up an ordered structure be determined by the physical properties of the whole system. Others [31]) have carried this point forward. It is the point of view postulated here that whatever the structure of the protein coats adjacent to the membrane, the skeletal phospholipid bilayer will always remain in-tact as long as the cell survives. Therefore, the "ice-like structures" envisaged, based on the electrostatics of the polar groups of the phospholipid bilayer, are essentially "bound" into the structural configuration of the cell independent of protein structures. Thus the point of view suggested by Szent-Gyorgyi [25]), that "biological functions may actually consist of the building and destruction of water structures" may not apply. Rather, bound water associated with proteins, but not associated with membrane structures, might very well perform this function. The conformation of bilayer membrane structures in all cells must lead to the ice-like structures described earlier.

5 *Summary*

The need for understanding the nature of "bound water" associated with biological membrane systems, is reemphasized. Current theoretical approaches to analyzing the aqueous milieu of biological surfaces via (1) chemical, (2) geometric and (3) statistical points of view, are briefly reviewed. Based on the fundamental structure of the phospholipid bilayer found in all membrane systems, the non-statistical electrostatic properties of the dipoles in the biological surface relative to the individual discrete water dipoles are evaluated. Three mathematical expressions are introduced which determine the nature of the "bound water" and "ice-like structures" present. Based on these equations, a quantitative definition of "ice-like structures" at the microscopic level is set forth.

6 *References*

[1] Love, R. M., *in*: *Cryobiology*, ed. Meryman, H. T., (1966);
Bratton, C. B., Hopkins, A. L., Weinberg, J. W., Science **147** (1965) 738;
Sussman, M. V., Chin, L., Science **151** (1966) 324.

[2] Kistler, S. S., J. Am. Chem. Soc. **58** (1936) 6.

[3] Parkes, A. S., New Scientist **7** (1960) 1057.

[4] Parkes, A. S., New Scientist **9** (1961) 810.

[5] Mazur, P., J. Gen. Physiol. **47** (1963) 347.

[6] Tikhov, G. A., J. Brit. Astron. Assoc. **65** (1955) 193.

[7] Ashworth, L. A. E., Green, C., Science **151** (1966) 210.

[8] Stoeckenius, W., Symp. Internatl. Soc. Cell Biol. **1** (Academic Press, N. Y., 1963) p. 349–367.

[9] Haydon, D. A., *in*: *Recent progress in surface science* **1**, ed. Danielli, J. F., Pankhurst, K. G. A., Riddiford, A. C. (Academic Press, N. Y., 1964) p. 116.

[10] Rudin, H., Mueller, P. D. D., Circulation **26** (1962) 1167.

[11] Brady, G. W., Krause, J. T., J. Chem. Phys. **27** (1957) 304; **28** (1958) 464;
Fernandez-Moran, H., Circulation **26** (1962) 1039.

[12] Pauling, L., Science **134** (1961) 15.

[13] Vogelhut-Featherstone, Nature **203** (1964) 1169.

[14] Hechter, O., Federation Proc. **24** [2] Part III, March-April, S-91 (1965).

[15] Warner, D. T., J. Theor. Biol. **1** (1961) 514.

[16] Scheraga, H. A., J. Chem. Phys. **36** (1962) 3382.

[17] Eyring, H., J. Phys. Chem. **68** (1964) 221.

[18] Scheraga, H. A., J. Phys. Chem. **66** (1962) 1773.

[19] Eyring, H., Implications of the chemical kinetics of some biological systems, *in*: *The present state of physics* (A.A.A.S., 1952) p. 189.

[20] Barlow, C. A., Jr., Ross MacDonald, J., J. Chem. Phys. **40** (1964) 1535.

[21] Scheraga, H. A., J. Chem. Phys. **36** (1962) 3401;
Depireaux, J., Nature **195** (1962) 699.

[22] Molyneux, T., Nature **202** (1964) 368.

[23] Pethica, B. A., Levine, S., Bell, G. M., J. Chem. Phys. **40** (1964) 230.

[24] Pethica, B. A., Brooks, J. H., Trans. Faraday Soc. **60** No. 493 Part 1 (1964) p. 1.

[25] Szent-Gyorgyi, A., *Bioenergetics* (Academic Press, N. Y., 1957).

[26] Klotz, I. M., Science **128** (1958) 815.

[27] Jacobson, B., J. Am. Chem. Soc. **77** (1955) 2919.

[28] Haurowitz, F., *Chemistry and biology of proteins* (Academic Press, N.Y., 1950).

[29] Gregor, H. F., Rec. Adv. Hormone Res. **16** (1960) 182.

[30] Bernal, J. D., Fowler, R. H., J. Chem. Phys. **1** (1933) 515.

[31] Frank, H. S., Evans, M. V., J. Chem. Phys. **13** (1945) 507.

Index